KEY STAGE ONE
SCOTTISH LEVELS A-B

NUMBER

KATHY HALL AND LYNETTE KELLY

Published by Scholastic Ltd,
Villiers House,
Clarendon Avenue,
Leamington Spa,
Warwickshire CV32 5PR
Text © 1995 Kathy Hall and Lynette Kelly
© 1995 Scholastic Ltd
567890   89012345

AUTHORS
KATHY HALL AND LYNETTE KELLY

EDITOR
CHRISTINE LEE

SERIES DESIGNER
LYNNE JOESBURY

DESIGNER
ANNA OLIWA/CAN DO DESIGN

ILLUSTRATIONS
MARY HALL

COVER ILLUSTRATION
GAY STURROCK

TECHNOLOGY CONSULTANT
MARTIN BLOWS

SCOTTISH 5-14 LINKS
MARGARET SCOTT AND SUSAN GOW

Designed using Aldus Pagemaker

British Library Cataloguing-in-Publication Data
A catalogue record for this book is available from the British
Library.

ISBN 0-590-53381-9

Contents

ACKNOWLEDGEMENTS

The publishers wish to acknowledge the invaluable assistance and advice given by Shelagh Bird and Gill Perry in compiling this book.

Introduction

Scholastic Curriculum Bank is a series for all primary teachers, providing both an essential planning tool for devising comprehensive schemes of work as well as an easily accessible and varied bank of practical, classroom-tested activities with photocopiable resources.

Designed to help planning for an implementation of progression, differentiation and assessment, *Scholastic Curriculum Bank* offers a structured range of stimulating activities with clearly-stated learning objectives that reflect the programmes of study, and detailed lesson plans that allow busy teachers to put the ideas into practice with the minimum amount of preparation time. The photocopiable sheets that accompany many of the activities provide ways of integrating purposeful application of knowledge and skills, differentiation, assessment and record-keeping.

Opportunities for formative assessment are highlighted where appropriate within the activities, while separate summative assessment activities give guidelines for analysis and subsequent action. Ways of using information technology for different purposes and within different contexts, as a tool for communicating and handling information and as a method for investigating, are integrated into the activities where appropriate and more explicit guidance is provided at the end of the book.

The series covers all the primary curriculum subjects with separate books for Key Stages 1 and 2/Scottish Levels A–B and C–E. It can be used as a flexible resource with any scheme to fulfil National Curriculum and Scottish 5–14 requirements and to provide children with a variety of different learning experiences that will lead to effective acquisition of skills and knowledge.

SCHOLASTIC CURRICULUM BANK MATHEMATICS

The Scholastic Curriculum Bank Mathematics books enable teachers to plan coverage of the primary mathematics curriculum and pupils to develop the required skills, knowledge and understanding through activities that promote mathematical thinking and ways of working.

There are two books for Key Stage 1/Scottish Levels A–B and two for Key Stage 2/Scottish Levels C–E.
▲ Number (including Handling Data);
▲ Shape, Space and Measures.

Using and Applying Mathematics is integrated into these contexts as required by the National Curriculum and these links are highlighted on the grid on pages 156–157.

Bank of activities

This book provides a bank of activities that can be used in many different ways – to form a framework for a scheme of work; to add breadth and variety to an existing scheme; to supplement a particular topic. The activities are designed to address a number of important areas of study.

Range

There is a range of activities provided, involving both first-hand experiences and the use of other sources of information. The activities allow pupils to develop mathematical language, select and use materials, and develop reasoning in the context of the areas of mathematics.

Opportunities for the use of calculators are provided for as a means to explore number and as a tool for calculating with realistic data.

The range of activities allows pupils to acquire the five elements of learning mathematics: facts, concepts, skills, strategies and attitudes.
▲ Facts are items of information which are unconnected and not supported by concepts, for example a telephone number or postcode.
▲ Concepts are ideas growing continually in the mind. They become richly interconnected and form a network of understanding for example, place, value or subtraction.
▲ Skills are mental or physical procedures often involving several stages, for example, using a calculator.
▲ Strategies are procedures for choosing which skills and

knowledge to use, for example, trial and improvement.
▲ Attitudes are developed in many ways. Positive attitudes to mathematics are necessary for future learning.

Communication skills

The activities aim to develop children's communication skills by encouraging them to:
▲ ask questions;
▲ explain their thinking;
▲ understand and use mathematical language;
▲ discuss their work;
▲ use a variety of forms of mathematical presentation;
▲ devise and refine their own ways of recording;
▲ present information and results clearly.

Mathematics in everyday life

Contexts used for the activities in these books have been chosen to be appropriate for the age of the pupils, familiar to their experience and relevant to their level of maturity.

Lesson plans

Detailed lesson plans, under clear headings, are given for each activity and provide teacher-ready material for immediate implementation in the classroom. The structure for each activity is as follows:

Activity title box

The information contained in the title box at the beginning of each activity outlines the following key aspects:
▲ *Activity title and learning objective:* For each activity there is a clearly stated learning objective which is given in bold italics. These learning objectives break down aspects of the programme of study into manageable, hierarchical, teaching and learning chunks, and their purpose is to aid planning for progression. These objectives can be easily referenced to the National Curriculum and Scottish 5–14 requirements by using the overview grids at the end of this introduction (pages 9 to 12).
▲ *Class organisation/Likely duration:* Icons 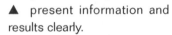 and  signpost the suggested group sizes for each activity and the approximate amount of time required to complete it.

Previous skills/knowledge needed

Information is given here when it is necessary for the children to have acquired specific knowledge or skills prior to carrying out the activity.

Key background information

The information given in this section is intended to support teachers' subject knowledge of mathematics and to show how the mathematics is incorporated into the activity where necessary.

Preparation

Advice is given for those occasions where it is necessary for the teacher to orientate the pupils to the activity or to prepare materials, or set up a display or activity ahead of time.

Resources needed

All the materials needed to carry out the activity are listed so that either pupils or teacher can gather them together easily before the beginning of the teaching session.

What to do

Easy to follow, step-by-step instructions are given for carrying out the activity including, where appropriate, suggested questions for the teacher to ask the pupils to help instigate discussion and stimulate investigation.

Suggestion(s) for extension/support

Wherever feasible, the activities lend themselves to easy differentiation. In all cases, suggestions are provided as to how each activity can be modified for the less able or extended for the more able.

Assessment opportunities

Each activity has clearly staged assessment opportunities which relate directly to the learning objectives for that activity and provide the framework for ongoing assessment. By taking advantage of these assessment opportunities teachers can reassure themselves that the stated learning objectives have been achieved. This important knowledge will ensure that teachers are sufficiently informed about children's learning and progress to be able to plan a curriculum and learning experiences that meet their present learning needs and support future progress within the mathematics curriculum.

Opportunities for IT

Where opportunities for IT present themselves, these are briefly outlined with reference to particularly suitable types of program. The chart on pages 158–159 presents specific areas of IT covered in the activities, together with more detailed support on how to apply particular types of program. Selected lesson plans serve as models for other activities by providing more comprehensive guidance on the application of IT.

Display ideas

Where relevant, display ideas are incorporated into activity plans and illustrated with examples.

Reference to photocopiable sheets

Where activities include photocopiable worksheets, small reproductions of these are included in the lesson plans together with guidance notes for their use, and, where appropriate, suggested answers.

Summative assessment

There will be key points in time when teachers wish to take an overview of each pupil's achievement in mathematics. Consequently this chapter provides a number of specific assessment activities related to the main areas of study covered elsewhere in the book that can be used for formative and/or summative assessment purposes. These activities provide focused assessment opportunities across a range of interrelated learning objectives which will form the basis, alongside other types of evidence, for the major summative assessment at the end of the key stage against the level descriptions. In these lesson plans guidance is given for what to look for from the pupils and what that might mean for their future learning of mathematics.

Using and applying mathematics

Aspects of using and applying mathematics are integral to each activity. Using and applying mathematics cannot be taught separately from the other areas of mathematics. It cannot exist alone. It must be set in the context of mathematical content. It should be thought of more as a teaching methodology and a mathematical process than as a distinct and separate content area. The teaching methodology relies strongly on the ability to challenge pupils through questioning and extending tasks. Pupils need to be encouraged to ask questions and follow alternative suggestions to support the development of reasoning. Therefore, on pages 156–157 a grid relating each activity to using and applying mathematics is provided. This grid will enable teachers to ensure that sufficient time and attention is paid to this central area of mathematics.

Photocopiable sheets

Many of the activities are accompanied by photocopiable sheets. For some activities, there may be more than one version of a worksheet, or a sheet will be 'generic' with a facility for the teacher to fill in the appropriate task in order to provide differentiation by task. Other sheets may be more open-ended to provide differentiation by outcome. The photocopiable sheets provide purposeful activities that are ideal for assessment and for keeping as records in pupils' portfolios of work.

Cross-curricular links

Cross-curricular links are identified on a simple grid cross-referencing the particular areas of study in mathematics to the programmes of study in other subjects of the curriculum.

NUMBER AT KEY STAGE 1

It is very probable that most people, if asked what are the elements of mathematics, would include the idea of number in their response. It is very probable that everyone would refer to 'numbers' and 'counting' if asked what are the ideas with which mathematics begins. Number is involved in virtually all aspects of mathematics and in that sense could be said to be the most important mathematical concept for the young learner to grasp. More importantly, though, number concepts underpin many everyday activities and ideas: recognising and making well-defined collections of objects (sets), matching (one-to-one correspondence), counting, equivalence and so

on. An appreciation of number is essential for coping efficiently with our world. It is not surprising, therefore, that number is a key component of the mathematics curriculum at Key Stage 1. This book aims to support the teacher in developing young learners' number concepts by providing activities which use the children's environment and everyday experiences. The activities reflect the range of knowledge, skills and concepts in number to be taught at Key Stage 1 and can be summarised as follows:

▲ sorting, classifying and matching: deciding how objects are alike or different, sorting objects into subsets, matching objects one-to-one, identifying classifying attributes, comparing the number of objects in two or more sets;

▲ counting and ordinality: matching number names in one-to-one correspondence to a set of objects, ordering to position e.g. first, second, third etc;

▲ cardinality and conservation: identifying sets with the same number of objects, recognising that the number remains the same regardless of the arrangement of the objects in the set;

▲ the language of number including symbol recognition: understanding the terms associated with the activities of number, e.g. sharing, sorting, matching, counting, the same, different, odd, even etc, recognising numbers by sight and sound;

▲ pattern: recognising and creating patterns, using the structure of patterns to predict and recognise numbers;

▲ place value: appreciating that the position of a digit in a number indicates its value;

▲ number operations: adding, subtracting, multiplying and dividing.

These skills and concepts are reflected in the structure of this book which is divided into four main sections:

▲ Number structure and place value – in which the activities are on the number system and fractions;

▲ Number relationships – in which the activities are on patterns, number facts and special numbers;

▲ Calculations and problem solving – in which the activities are on operations, problems and checking;

▲ Data handling.

Learning objective	PoS/AO	Content	Type of activity	Page
Number system and place value				
To be able to count numbers up to 10 accurately. To be able to match sets according to the number of elements within them. To be able to compare sets and to identify sets with fewer elements.	Count collections of objects 2 (a). *Mathematics 5-14. Range and type of numbers, level A.*	Cards with between 1 and 10 animals, 4 types of animals. Matching Game.	Pair or small group activity based on a game using playing cards.	14
To be able to use the language of ordinal number confidently and correctly.	Recognise sequences 2 (a). *As above, level A.*	Collection of toys. Group discussion. Each child draws one animal, to form a book. Discuss ordinality.	A group of 6 are involved in a discussion-based activity.	15
To be able to read and write 2- and 3- digit numbers correctly.	Read and write numbers 2 (b). *As above, level A.*	Number cards 0–9 (3 sets). Make a 2-digit number, other child states the number. 3-digit, one child says the number, other makes it with cards.	A playing card-based game for pairs or groups of four children.	16
To be able to identify correctly the largest number in a group of four 2-digit numbers. To be able to order sets of four 2-digit numbers according to their value.	Order numbers 2 (b). *As above, level B.*	Number cards 0–99. Game for four. Each child turns over a card; person with the highest gets 4 counters; next highest gets 3 etc. One with most wins.	A playing card-based game for groups or four children.	18
To develop an early understanding of the significance of the position of a digit in the place value system. To recognise that the decimal place value system is based on groups of 10.	Developing an understanding that the position of a digit signifies its value 2 (b). *As above, level B.*	1p, 10p and £1 coins. One child throws dice, collect 1p until can exchange 10 for 10p, then continue and exchange everything for £1.	A board game for a pair of children.	19
To recognise the effect of adding 10 and 100 to a number. To be able to set up a constant on a basic calculator.	Developing an understanding that the position of a digit signifies its value 2 (b). *As above, level B.*	Dot to dots numbered. +10 +100 one blank picture 1, 11, 21, 31 etc. 5, 15, 25, 35 etc. 9, 19, 29, 39 etc.	An individual calculator activity that could be undertaken by a large group at a time.	20
To be able to convert prices to decimal notation.	Recognise in context simple fractions 2 (c). *As above, level C.*	Using price tags, children compare and convert prices e.g. £1.50 and 150p etc. They use money cards.	Practical task involving large group discussion and then pair work.	23
To begin to recognise that a whole can be partitioned into equal parts. To recognise halves and quarters of a whole.	Recognise in context simple fractions 2 (c). *Mathematics 5-14, level B.*	Dividing food into 2 and 4 equal parts.	Large group in teacher-led discussion.	26
To recognise halves of a whole.	Recognise in context simple fractions 2 (c). *As above, level B.*	Matching halves of symmetrical shapes.	Practical activity for pair of children.	27
To recognise that sets can be partitioned into equal parts. To be able to partition sets up to 12 into 2 or 4 equal parts.	Recognise in context simple fractions 2 (c). *As above, level B.*	Finding fractions of a set of objects.	Practical activity for small group or pairs.	28
To begin to appreciate the need for a range of fractions, specifically, to appreciate that halves and quarters are inadequate for partitioning some sets. To begin to become aware of the need for the fraction one third.	Recognise in context simple fractions 2 (c). *As above, level C.*	Problem solving task in groups of three: share objects equally, some of which are not easily partitioned into thirds, followed by individual work.	Problem-solving activity for groups of three, then individual activity.	29
To recognise different ways of representing the same amount using different fractions and fractions of different sets.	Recognise in context simple fractions 2 (c). *As above, level B.*	Sharing sets of cubes into groups of various sizes, e.g. dividing set of 16 cubes into 4 groups so each group has the same number. Recording this using fractions and numbers from photocopiables.	Practical activity for pairs using cubes and fraction number cards.	31
Number relationships				
To be able to recognise and describe patterns on objects.	Use repeating patterns to develop ideas of regularity and sequencing 3 (a). *Mathematics 5-14 Patterns and sequences, level A.*	Collection of patterned artefacts in a bag. Each child chooses one and says something about it. Group talk. Followed up by making repeating patterns in Art, Music (clapping etc.) and PE (movement patterns).	Large or small group discussion-based activity followed by further work in Art or PE.	34
To be able to recognise and describe a sequence of events. To be able to predict the next stage in a sequence.	Count in steps of different sizes 2 (a). *As above, level A.*	Getting dressed. Group discussion first. Then sorting into order group of cards showing a teddy in various stages of dress. Children make up their own pattern.	Large group discussion followed by exploratory work in pairs and work-sheet based activity.	35

NUMBER

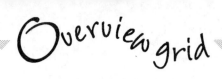

Learning objective	PoS/AO	Content	Type of activity	Page
To be able to recognise numbers from 1 to 10 placed in a variety of arrays. To be able to place up to 10 counters in systematic spatial patterns.	Count collection of objects, checking the total 2 (a). *As above, level A.*	Using 3, 4 counters, etc, to make patterns. Making up number patterns using blank domino cards. Using the cards to play snap.	Large group discussion followed by small group activity and game in pairs.	37
To be able to partition a number. To be able to order addition sums in a systematic way. To begin to recognise the value of pattern in completing addition calculations.	Patterns in addition 3 (b). *As above, level A.*	Explore a number of ways to add two numbers to make, say, 6. Then go on to building up larger numbers, then three numbers.	Small group investigation. Individual work followed by large or small group discussion.	38
To be able to find several subtraction calculations that have the same answer. To recognise patterns in subtraction calculations. To be able to order subtraction sums in a systematic way.	Patterns in subtraction 3 (b). *As above, level A.*	Explore number pairs with a difference of two (up to 20).	Small group work followed by individual investigation.	39
To recognise patterns of multiples up to 5 × 5 and later 10 × 10. To be able to use patterns of multiples to help solve multiplication tables.	Patterns of multiples 3 (b). *Multiply, level B.*	Explore multiples patterns using 5 × 5 grid and 10 × 10 grid. Then children go on to make their own patterns using a blank grid.	A game for two players.	40
To be able to recall number facts using addition and subtraction to 12 quickly and accurately.	Known addition and subtraction facts to 20. 3 (c). *Mathematics 5-14 Add and subtract, level B.*	Children total scores from throw of two dice, and find this number on a board of numbers. The player who covers the most numbers wins.	Large group discussion followed by individual activity.	42
To build up a knowledge of the relationship between number facts. To be able to identify several number facts related to a single answer.	Develop mental methods of finding new results. 3 (c). *As above, level B.*	The number of the day is selected, say, 15. Children think of a range of calculations which result in 15. Talk focusing on strategies used. A systematic approach is encouraged.	A variety of tasks and games for pairs.	43
To know the number facts in the 2, 5 and 10 times tables.	Learn multiplication and division fact relating to the 2s, 5s, 10s. 3 (c). *Multiply, level B.*	Children have sets of cards with 2, 5 and 10 times tables (answers and sums). They play snap, use the calculator, test each other and so on.	Practical work in pairs followed by whole class discussion.	44
To be able to predict unknown number facts using a doubling technique.	Use the multiplication and division facts in the 2s, 5s and 10s to learn other facts. 3 (c). *Multiply and divide, level B.*	Children use cards to build up the facts about 5×. From this they are encouraged to establish the facts for 10×.	Practical, individual work followed by whole class discussion.	46
To recognise that subtraction is the inverse of addition. To be able to use subtraction as the inverse of addition.	Use the fact that subtraction is the inverse of addition 3 (d). *Add and subtract.*	Using a photocopiable sheet with a series of squares, children select a starting number and add on another to the previous number until they come to the middle square, then continue by subtracting that number.	Practical, individual work followed by whole class discussion.	47
To recognise that division is the inverse of multiplication. To be able to use division as the inverse of multiplication.	Learn multiplication and division facts relating to the 2s, 5s and 10s. 3 (c). *Multiply and divide, level B.*	Using a photocopiable sheet with a series of squares, children select a starting number and multiply the previous number by another number until they come to the middle square, then continue by dividing the number.	Group of 4 to 6 children are involved in a practical, discussion-orientated activity.	48
To recognise that zero represents an empty set and its use as place holder in the place value system.	Develop an understanding that the position of a digit signifies its value. 2 (b). *Range and type of numbers, level A.*	Collection of tins with between 0 and 5 items. Children shake the tin and guess the number of counters. Attention is focused on the empty tin.	Discussion based on practical activity and a game.	49
To be able to identify odd and even numbers.	Recognise sequences including odd and even numbers. 2 (a). *As above, level A.*	Using odd and even numbers of cubes to build towers. Discussion about how many cubes you need to build 2 towers of equal height. Playing a game in pairs using 2 dice.	Discussion based on practical activity.	50
To be able to recognise square numbers up to 100.	Exploring further patterns using multiplication. 3 (b). *Multiply, level B.*	Arranging different numbers of counters into squares. Distinguishing between numbers which are square and numbers which are not square.	Discussion based on practical activity.	51

Learning objective	PoS/AO	Content	Type of activity	Page
To be able to establish several methods of arranging rectangular numbers such as 12, 24 and 36 in arrays.	Exploring further patterns using multiplication. 3 (b). *As above, level B.*	Children try to arrange different numbers of counters and rectangles. They distinguish between numbers which are rectangular and numbers which are not rectangular.	Discussion based on practical activity in pairs.	52
To recognise the effect of multiplying by 1, 10 and later 100.	Recognising that the position of the digit signifies its value. 2 (b). *As above, level C.*	Pairs of children throw a dice (later two and three dice) and multiply the number by 10 (later 100). They discuss the effect of multiplying by 10 and by 100.	Discussion based on practical activity in pairs.	53
To begin to recognise negative numbers and to know that they represent amounts below zero.	Recognise and use in context negative numbers. 2 (c). *Range and type of numbers, level E.*	Pairs of children, using a calculator, experiment by subtracting a larger number from a smaller one.	Discussion based on practical activity in groups of 4 to 6 children.	54

Calculations and problem solving

Learning objective	PoS/AO	Content	Type of activity	Page
To recognise when addition and subtraction should be used. To be able to add /subtract within 10 quickly and accurately. To be able to use a variety of words and phrases to describe addition and subtraction.	Develop a variety of methods for adding and subtracting. 3 (d). *Add and subtract, level A.*	4 to 6 children engage in a discussion involving a picture of a toy shop and lots of small toys. They make up stories about how many toys were bought/sold.	Discussion based on a shopping activity in groups of 4 to 6 children.	56
To be able to subtract confidently and accurately within 20.	Know subtraction facts to twenty. 3 (c). *Subtract, level B.*	4 to 6 children engage in a discussion using lots of cards with pictures of toys plus their prices, all 20p or less. They 'buy' various toys and receive change from a 20p coin.	Discussion based on a shopping activity in groups of 4 to 6 children.	57
To be able to subtract within 100 using apparatus.	Develop a variety of methods for subtraction. 3 (d). *Subtract, level C.*	4 to 6 children engage in a discussion using cards with pictures of toys plus their prices, all £1 or less. They 'buy' toys and receive change from a pound coin.		59
To recognise that multiplication is equivalent to repeated addition. To be able to complete simple multiplication calculations through repeated addition.	Understand the operation of multiplication. 4 (b). *Multiply, level B.*	4 to 6 children listen to a story. On the turn of a page a number of objects are placed on the table (e.g. 2p). Discussion follows to reinforce the notion of repeated addition.	Discussion based on a story.	60
To recognise that division is equivalent to repeated subtraction. To be able to complete simple division calculations through repeated subtraction.	Understand the operation of division as repeated subtraction. 4 (b). *Divide, level B.*	4 to 6 children listen to you reading a story. On the turn of a page a number of objects are removed from the table (e.g. 2p). Discussion follows to reinforce the notion of division as repeated subtraction.	Discussion based on a story.	61
To be able to use each of the four operations in simple situations. To be able to combine two operations in a calculation.	Understand the operations of addition, subtraction, multiplication and division. 4 (a and b). *Add and subtract, levelB. Multiply and divde, level B.*	4 to 6 children play a game involving a range of calculations based on addition, subtraction, multiplication and division.	4 to 6 children play a game.	63
To be able to combine prices up to one pound. To be able to handle coins effectively.	Understand addition. 4 (a). *Add and subtract, level B.*	4 to 6 involved in a shopping activity using the class shop.	Practical activity based in class shop.	64
To be able to give change from one pound. To calculate change in a variety of ways.	Understand subtraction as taking away and comparison. 4 (a). *Money, level B.*	4 to 6 involved in a shopping activity using the class 'café.	Practical activity based on shopping.	65
To be able to calculate multiplication sums using repeated addition in 2s, 5s and 10s.	Understand multiplication. 4 (b). *Multiply, level B.*	4 to 6 involved in a 'stock-taking' activity involving multiple packs of items.	Practical activity based on counting multiple packs of objects.	66
To begin to calculate division sums using objects. To begin to be able to deal appropriately with remainders.	Understand division as sharing and repeated subtraction, dealing with remainders. 4 (b). *Divide, level B.*	4 to 6 involved in a sharing activity where the number of objects to be shared divide equally first, then involve remainde	Practical activity based on sharing.	68

11

Learning objective	PoS/AO	Content	Type of activity	Page
To be able to estimate the answer to a simple addition sum.	Gain a feel for the appropriate size of an answer. 4 (d). *Add, level B.*	Pairs of children throw three dice and estimate the answer. A calculator is used to check and estimates and answers are recorded.	A board game for 2 to 4 players.	69
To recognise that counting on and addition provide a check on one another. To be able to use addition as a method for checking counting on.	Begin to check answers in different ways. 4 (d). Mathematics 5-14. *Add and subtract, level B.*	2 to 4 children takes turns to throw two dice and add on or count on the second score. Numerical and dot dice used.	A small group discussion based practical activity.	70
To recognise that calculations can be checked by reference to the original concrete situation.	Begin to check answers in different ways. 4 (d). *Add and subtract, level A.*	Pairs of children take turns to remove objects from a bag while the partner estimates how many are left. The result is checked by counting how many are left.	A small group game using calculators.	71
To be able to check known multiplication facts on a calculator.	Begin to check answers in different ways. 4 (d). Use a basic calculator. 3 (e). *Multiply, level B.*	2 to 4 children have up to 10 seconds to find the 'right' sum for the given 'answer'. They match sums and answers and test each other through a game and check answers using a calculator.	Investigative activity based on group collaboration and involving addition and subtraction.	72
To be able to check addition through the use of subtraction.	Begin to check answers in different ways. 4 (d). *Add, level A.*	2 to 4 children work together to move from, say, 2 to 10 adding on different numbers. They check the 'journey' by using the opposite operation.	A large or small group activity using real data.	73
To be able to check addition through adding a set of data in a different order.	Begin to check answers in different ways. 4 (d). *Add, level B.*	Large groups or whole class compile a data set of class members. They add the column of figures from the bottom up and check by adding from the top down.	A large or small group activity using real data.	74
To be able to check addition through grouping data in more convenient sets.	Begin to check answers in different ways. 4 (d). *Add, level B.*	Large group or whole class compile a data set. Children are encouraged to group the data in different ways before adding.	Practical activity based on throwing three dice and using a calculator.	75

Handling Data

Learning objective	PoS/AO	Content	Type of activity	Page
To be able to sort simple sets of objects using one or two criteria.	Sort and classify a set of objects. 5 (a). Mathematics 5-14. *Information handling, collecting and organising, level A.*	Large/small group of children working with the teacher group themselves into different sets, followed up by pair work classifying objects according to a range of attributes.	Large or small group practical activity.	78
To be able to sort objects using Carroll or Venn diagrams.	Use increasing range of charts, diagrams, tables and graphs.5(b). *As above.*	Children group themselves according to a range of criteria. They represent these sets in Carroll and/ or Venn diagrams.	Teacher-directed large or small group discussion and demonstration of different types of diagrams.	81
To be able to use tallying when collecting data.	Collect data. 5 (b). *Collecting and organising, level B.*	Children collect data about themselves and use tallying in their recording of these data.	Data gathering and recording exercise.	83
To be able to present simple data in a two-way table.	Use an increasing range of charts, diagrams, tables and graphs. 5 (b). *Collecting, organising and displaying, level C.*	Children collect data about foods and drink they like and present this information in a two-way table.	Data gathering and recording exercise.	84
To be able too present data in a simple block graph. To be able to interpret data presented in a simple block graph.	Use an increasing range of charts, diagrams, tables and graphs. 5 (b). *Collecting, organising and displaying, level B.*	Children collect data about themselves and present this information in a block graph.	Data gathering and recording exercise.	86
To be able to present data in a graph using a simple scale on one of the axes. To be able to interpret data presented in a graph using a simple scale on one of the axes.	Use increasing range of charts, diagrams, tables and graphs. 5 (b). *Displaying and interpreting, level B.*	Children collect data about themselves and present this information in a graph using a simple scale.	Data gathering and recording exercise.	87

Number system place and value

An understanding of the structure of our number system and place value permeates all elements of number work.

Getting to grips with the number system includes recognising the relationship between number symbols and numbers, recognising and using specific symbols and vocabulary, understanding cardination (understanding the value of a number, e.g. 5 means five of something) and ordination (understanding something's position in a series, e.g. 1st, 2nd, 3rd) as parts of a single system and understanding the place value.

An inadequate understanding of place value is very often what hinders further numerical progress in the primary school and beyond. To ensure children grasp a sound understanding of the structure of number, it is essential to provide them with plenty of practical activities and to promote lots of discussion.

Despite the introduction of the calculator, vulgar fractions continue to be used in everyday life especially simple fractions such as halves, quarters and three quarters. The use of appropriate, meaningful words and phrases in discussing fractions can play a key role in building up sound concepts.

The activities in this section look at the number system and fractions. The activities relating to fractions begin on page 26 with 'Equal parts'.

Number system and place value

MATCH THE ANIMALS

To be able to count accurately up to 10; to be able to match sets according to the number of elements within them; to be able to compare sets and to identify sets with more or fewer elements.

†† *Pairs.*
🕐 *30 minutes.*

Previous skills/knowledge needed
Children should be able to undertake tasks involving one-to-one correspondence.

Key background information
Sorting, classifying and matching sets according to the number of elements contained in them provides the kind of concrete, first-hand experience necessary for developing the young learner's understanding of the number system.

Preparation
Copy photocopiable pages 98 and 99 directly on to card or mount copies on to card. If possible, colour them and then laminate them or cover them with clear adhesive plastic film. Cut up into individual cards. Make sure you have made enough sets for each pair.

Resources needed
For each pair: a set of animal cards cut from photocopiable sheets 98 and 99.

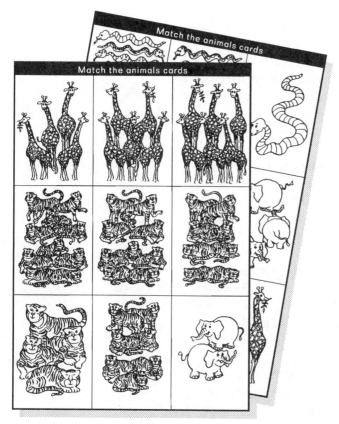

What to do
Shuffle the cards and spread them on the table face up. Discuss with the children how the cards show pictures of different animals. Ensure they understand that there are pictures of snakes, giraffes, elephants and tigers and ask different children to point out the different animals.

Now tell the children that the animals are all mixed up. Explain that they must help to put the animals back into the right groups so that all the elephants are together, all the tigers are together, all the giraffes are together and all the snakes are together. Ask the children to work in pairs to sort the cards so that all the same animals are grouped together. Once they have done this, ask them to say what they have done.

Now ask the children to sort each set of animals so that they are in order according to the number of animals on each card, placing the cards in a line along the table. For example, the set of snakes should be as follows:

Again, encourage the children to say what they have done. Question the children about how many snakes, for example, there are on different cards. Get them to count out the number of snakes and encourage them to make the following kinds of statements: 'There are *more* snakes on this card [pointing to the card with 10 snakes] *than* on this card' [pointing to the card with 7 snakes] and 'There are *fewer* snakes on this card [pointing to the card with 1 snake] *than* on this card' [pointing to the card with 7 snakes].

Next ask the children to imagine that the animals wish to make new friends. Can the children help them? Can they find cards with the same number of different animals? Ask the children to sort the cards into sets so that each set contains cards which show the same number of animals. Again, they should place the cards in a line along the table. For example, the first two sets will be laid out on the table as follows:

As before, encourage the children to say what they have done and to discuss the number in each set using statements such as 'I have *the same* number of giraffes *as* elephants.' Help them to discover that there is only one card (in the set) with 3 animals, i.e. 3 elephants, and only one card (in the set) with 9 animals, i.e. 9 tigers.

Remove the cards with no pair (3 elephants and 9 tigers). Then shuffle the cards and spread them out face downwards on the table. Ask the children to play a matching game where they turn over two cards at a time trying to make a pair. If a child is successful in making a pair he or she removes the cards from the table and has another go. If not, play moves to the second child. The player with the most pairs of cards at the end is the winner.

Suggestion(s) for extension

Encourage each pair of children to join with another pair, share their cards and go through the above tasks again. Encourage the groups of four to sort the cards according to different types of numbers: odd numbers of animals, even numbers of animals; less than 5, greater than 4; and so on.

Suggestions(s) for support

Limit the number of cards so that you only use the cards with up to 5 animals. Most children should then be able to do all the above tasks as the sorting becomes easier and more manageable. Having done this, they can then proceed to using cards with 6 to 10 animals. Get the children to draw their own sets of animals and write the corresponding numeral under each set.

Assessment opportunities

Observe individual children as they count the animals on the cards. Do they do this accurately? Note which children, if any, need further practice in counting to 10. Also note their use of language in making comparisons, such as 'fewer than', 'more than' and 'the same as'. Do they use this language appropriately and confidently?

Opportunities for IT

Many computers have simple Pelmanism software which enables children to reinforce their matching skills using a computer. The best software allows the teacher to select the number of pictures to be matched, or even allows teachers to set up their own picture cards.

Display ideas

Help the children to mount their sets, for example, their 'same number sets' on to a larger sheet of card, using Blu-tack so that other arrangements can be made later.

Reference to photocopiable sheets

Photocopiable pages 98 and 99 offer children a set of animal cards which can be sorted in various ways.

CUDDLY TOYS

To be able to use the language of ordinal number confidently and correctly.

†† *Six children.*

🕐 *30–40 minutes.*

Previous skills/knowledge needed

Children should be able to undertake tasks involving one-to-one correspondence.

Preparation

Before doing this activity, give the children lots of opportunities to hear and respond to language associated with ordinal numbering. For example, in a PE session or in the classroom, use naturally occurring opportunities to emphasise the following terminology in relation to the children's own actions: first, second, third and so on, and last, next, before, and after.

Resources needed

Six soft toys, a tray (or any container that can be used as a 'bed' for the toys), a table, an A4 sheet of paper per child, pencils, felt-tipped pens, word processor (optional), glue, materials for making a group book.

What to do

Arrange for the group of six children to sit round a table so that they can work together.

Place the six toys in the 'bed'. Encourage the children to give a name to each one – they may wish to use their own names. Ask the children to imagine that the toys are asleep in bed and that they have to watch carefully to see who is the first to get out of bed. Take one toy out of the 'bed' and stand it on the table, then encourage the children to respond by saying, for example, 'Teddy is the *first* to get up'. Remove another toy and encourage a further response, such as 'Lucy is the *second* to get up'. Continue until all six toys are standing in a row on the table, encouraging children to use the ordinal language throughout.

Help the children to discuss what happened by using questions such as:
▲ Who was the last to get up?
▲ Who was the first to get up?
▲ Who was next?
▲ Who got up before Snowey?
▲ Who got up after Bonnie?

Make sure that each child has also asked one question for the other children to answer.

Next get each child to draw and colour a picture of one of the toys on A4 paper. Underneath the picture they should write a sentence using the ordinal language, e.g. 'Teddy is the first' and so on. Alternatively, the children could use the word processor to type their sentences and then glue them under their pictures. Collect all the finished pictures together and make a book to stick them in. The book can then be used to discuss ordinality.

Suggestion(s) for extension
Get the children to add four more toys, and thus continue using ordinal language to ten.

Suggestion(s) for support
Retain the activity in the above format but use only three toys, so that the amount of ordinal language involved is reduced.

Assessment opportunities
Note individual children's fluency, confidence and accuracy in using the language of ordinal numbers to six. Identify any children who may need further first-hand experiences. Note whether there are any children in the group who seemed to appreciate the relevant language but who did not take the opportunity to use it.

Opportunities for IT
Children could use a word processor to write their sentences using ordinal language. Alternatively a concept keyboard could be linked to the word processor with a mixture of words and pictures included on the overlay so that children could select the relevant presses to such sentences as 'Teddy is the first'.

Children could use a simple DTP or word processor to make a number book, mixing pictures and words together.

Each page could present a different number in large numerals and the text. Children could then select an appropriate number of objects to make the set. The objects could be drawn by the children using a simple art package or selected from simple clip art collections. The finished book could be displayed in the class.

Display ideas
The finished book can be shared with other children in the class and displayed in a prominent, accessible place in the classroom with the 'bed' and soft toys.

BUILDING 2-DIGIT NUMBERS

To be able to read and write 2- and 3-digit numbers correctly.
†† *Pairs or groups of four.*
🕑 *30–35 minutes.*

Previous skills/knowledge needed
The children should appreciate cardinality and conservation, that is, they should be able to identify sets which contain the same number of objects and recognise that the number in the set remains the same, regardless of the arrangement of the objects.

Key background information
Developing an appreciation of place value, i.e. that the position of a digit in a number indicates its value, underlies this activity.

Preparation
Copy photocopiable page 100 directly on to card or mount copies on to card. Laminate or cover the cards with clear adhesive plastic film and cut out the individual number cards. Make two sets of number cards from 0–9 for each pair or group of four.

Resources needed
For each pair or group of four: two sets of number cards from 0–9, writing materials and paper.

What to do
Organise the children so that they are seated in groups of four, and distribute the two sets of 0–9 cards to each pair or group.

Explain that you want the children to work together using the cards to make 2-digit numbers. Encourage them to record their results on paper. Ask them to identify the smallest 2-digit number they have made. Could they make a smaller 2-digit number than this one? Get them to look again for the smallest possible 2-digit number from their set of numbers. If they can find a smaller number, they should note down this one on paper.

Then ask them to identify the biggest 2-digit number they have made. Could they make a bigger 2-digit number than this one? Get them to look again for the biggest possible 2-digit number from their set of numbers, and if they find one they should then note it down.

Ask one child in the pair or group to collect the cards, shuffle them and then spread them face down on the table. The children can then play a game, the object of which is to make the biggest possible number. The children should take turns to select two cards from the pile, turn them over and make a 2-digit number. They should record each number on paper and the child who manages to make the biggest number is the winner. Let the children play this game several times and then change the rules so that the winner is the person who makes the lowest number.

Finally, get one child in the pair or group to specify a 2-digit number for the other(s) to make using the cards.

Throughout the activity, encourage the children to say the 2-digit number they make each time, for example, 'twenty-nine', rather than the separate single-digit numbers, 'a two and a nine'.

Building 2-digit number cards		
0	1	2
3	4	5
6	7	8
	9	

Suggestion(s) for extension

Adopting the same approach as outlined in the main activity, let the children make and record 3-digit numbers using three sets of number cards.

Suggestion(s) for support

Work on single-digit numbers using one set of number cards from 0–9. Let the children sequence them from the smallest to the largest, then from the largest to the smallest.

Reshuffle the cards and place them face up on the table. Ask the children to pick out the largest number, the smallest number, a number bigger than 7, a number smaller than 3, and so on.

Having worked like this with single-digit numbers, encourage them to make 2-digit numbers by using one set of cards. Discuss the numbers they make by saying, for example, 'What is this number?' Encourage the use of the name of the number throughout, for example, emphasise the number as *twelve* as opposed to 'a one and a two'.

Then ask questions such as 'Is 12 bigger than 1?', 'Is it bigger than 2?' and so on.

Assessment opportunities

Note individual children's confidence and speed in making the numbers and observe whether they can apply the correct language. For example, 'From a 4 and a 3 I can make 43.'

Display ideas

Help the children to display their results. For example, they might make a chart showing the various numbers they have

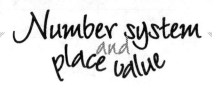

made. This could be captioned:
Numbers from 2 sets of number cards from 0–9
The biggest 2-digit number you can make is 99.
The smallest 2-digit number you can make is 00.

Reference to photocopiable sheets

Photocopiable page 100 provides number cards from 0–9.

LARGEST NUMBER WINS

To be able to identify correctly the largest number in a group of four 2-digit numbers; to be able to order sets of four 2-digit numbers according to their value.

†† *A group of four children.*

🕐 *30–40 minutes.*

Previous skills/knowledge needed

Children need to know what a 2-digit number is.

Preparation

Copy photocopiable pages 101 to 105 directly on to card or mount copies on to card. Laminate or cover them with clear adhesive plastic film and cut out the individual number cards. Prepare one set of number cards (from 0–99) for each group. Copy four sets of photocopiable page 106 – one for each player.

Resources needed

A set of number cards from 0–99 from photocopiable sheets 101 to 105, 100 counters, recording sheet from photocopiable page 106, writing materials, calculator (optional).

What to do

Tell the children that they are going to play a number game. Shuffle the set of 0–99 cards and place them on the table in a pile, face down. Put a collection of counters (at least 100) in the middle of the table. Explain the rules of the game to the children, and tell them that each child in turn should take a card. They should then discuss which number is the highest. The child who has the highest number wins that game and should take four counters from the pile in the middle of the table. The player who got the next highest number should take three counters, the player who got the next highest number takes two counters, and the player who got the smallest number takes one counter. Explain that the children should record what happened using the recording sheet from photocopiable

page 106. Ask them to play ten games, keeping their counters and recording their results as they go along using the recording sheet. The player with the most counters at the end of ten games is the winner.

Alternatively, you might prefer to get the children to return their counters to the middle of the table after every game, in which case they might need to use a calculator to check who collected the most counters. You will only need 10 counters for this version.

Suggestion(s) for extension

Increase the number of players and change the number of counters accordingly for the winner. Alternatively, place three piles of single-digit number cards (made from photocopiable page 101) face down on the table, and ask the four players each to select one card from each pile, thus each making up a 3-digit number. The player with the largest 3-digit number should take four counters, the player with the next largest take three counters, and so on.

The game continues as before, with the winner being the person with the most counters after ten games. As before, the players should record their results as they go along, using photocopiable page 106.

Suggestion(s) for support

Make the game less complex in the beginning by grouping children in pairs and having each child take a card. In this case the person with the largest number should take two counters and the person with the smallest take one. Adapt photocopiable page 106 so that there are only two boxes in the last column and let the children use it to record the results of this game.

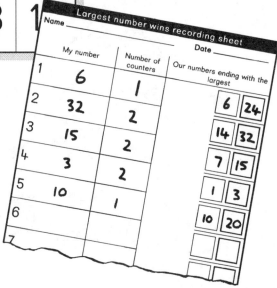

At the end of ten games the person with the most counters is the winner.

Give these children lots of practice making two 2-digit numbers before progressing to three players and selecting the largest 2-digit number from a set of three 2-digit numbers. Make a new recording sheet for the three 2-digit numbers.

Assessment opportunities

Along with your own observations of how accurately and confidently children can identify the largest and smallest numbers, you can use the recording sheet as evidence of their competence in achieving these learning objectives.

Display ideas

Each group of four children could be encouraged to make a booklet using their recording sheets. This could be displayed on the mathematics table for other children to look at.

Reference to photocopiable sheets

Photocopiable pages 101 to 105 offer children a set of 0–99 number cards which can be used in the game. Photocopiable page 106 can be used for recording the results of the game. Photocopiable page 101 with numbers from 0–9 can be used in the extension activity and photocopiable page 106 for recording the results can be used in the supporting activity.

RACE TO £1

To develop an early understanding of the significance of the position of a digit in the place value system; to recognise that the decimal place value system is based on groups of 10.

†† *Pairs.*

🕐 *30–40 minutes.*

Previous skills/knowledge needed

Children need to appreciate ordinality and to know what a 2-digit number is. They need to have had lots of experience of 'shopping' in the class shop and exchanging money for differently-priced items up to the value of one pound.

Preparation

Prepare a baseboard for each child by copying photocopiable page 107 directly on to card or mounting copies on card.

The baseboard could then be coloured in if required and finally laminated or covered with clear adhesive plastic film.

Resources needed

A baseboard made from photocopiable page 107 for each child, a collection of pennies, ten-pence and pound coins, a dice. For support activity: a dice marked with 1, 1, 2, 2, 3, 3.

What to do

Give each child a baseboard, then place the money in the middle of the table. Tell the children they are going to play a game and explain the rules as follows.

The first player throws a dice and picks up the corresponding number of pennies, say five, and places them on the 1p column of the baseboard. The second player then throws the dice and collects the relevant number of pennies and places them on his baseboard. They should continue to take it in turns to throw the dice, collect that amount of pennies, and fill up that column of their baseboard.

When a player reaches 10 or more, he should exchange ten pennies for a 10p coin and place it on the next column, i.e. the 10p column. The children should continue taking turns throwing the dice and collecting coins.

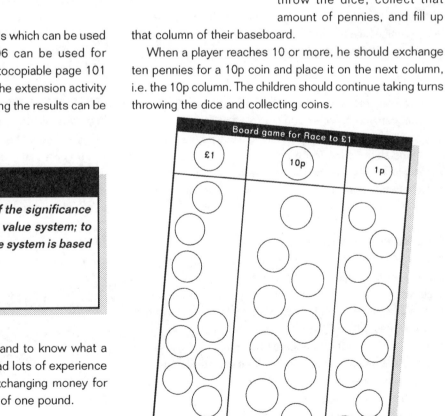

Board game for Race to £1

£1	10p	1p

Suggestion(s) for support

Make the game quicker and easier by having the players play to 10p using a dice marked with 1, 1, 2, 2, 3, 3.

Play exactly as above but the first person to exchange 10 pennies for one 10p coin is the winner. Give the children lots of practice playing this game before going on to the next stage.

Assessment opportunities

Through observing children play this game and noting how they respond to your questions, you can check which ones have grasped the significance that the position has for the value of a digit. To use this task for assessing a particular child or pair of children, make sure that you ask lots of questions of the kind suggested above in order to give them a chance to explain what they know and understand. You might also wish to use this game as a means of assessing the children's ability to use the correct notation (e.g. '£0.75 stands for seventy five pence').

Reference to photocopiable sheets

Photocopiable page 107 offers children a playing board which can be used in the game.

When a player reaches 10 or more he should exchange ten 10p coins for a pound coin and place it on the next column, i.e. the £1 column. This player is the winner.

Encourage discussion as they play, for example:
▲ How many pennies have you now?
▲ How many more do you need to reach ten?
▲ What can you do when you get to 10 or above?

As a player gets close to collecting a one pound coin, ask questions such as the following:
▲ How many 10p coins have you now?
▲ How many more do you need to make a pound?
▲ What can you do when you get to 10 or above?

Suggestion(s) for extension

After having finished the game, encourage each player to say and write down their final score. For example, the winner might write: 'I got one pound, two 10p coins and five pennies. This is the same as one pound twenty-five. I can write it down like this: £1.25.' The other player might state his result as follows: 'I did not get as far as one pound. I have seven 10p coins and two pennies. This is the same as seventy-two pence. I can write it down like this: 72p.' Introduce the children to another way of writing such an amount (£0.72).

This game could also be played by placing one pound coin in the pound column, then throwing the dice and taking away that amount, thus working back to zero. The first player to clear the baseboard would be the winner.

DOTTY NUMBERS

To recognise the effect of adding 10 and 100 to a number; to be able to set up a constant on a basic calculator.

†† *Whole class or smaller group.*

🕐 *30 minutes.*

Previous skills/knowledge needed

Children should be able to build 2-digit numbers and have some appreciation of place value. They should be familiar with using the number line for counting in 2s, 3s and so on.

Key background information

Children will need to know how to program the calculator to add and subtract a constant amount. For example, to set up a constant 'add 10' function, press the following keys:

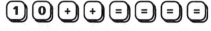

or

or (1)(0)(+)(=)(=)

The result should be 10, 20, 30, 40 etc.

To set up a constant 'add 100' function, press the following keys:

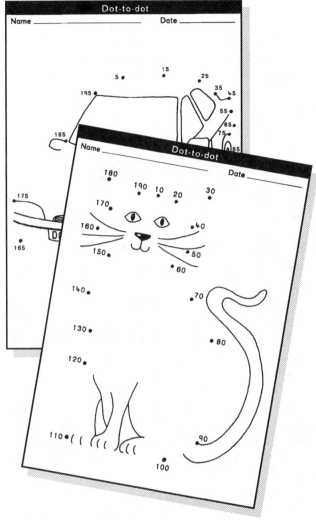

The result should be 100, 200, 300, 400, etc.

To set up a constant 'add 10' function beginning at 9, press the following keys, depending on the calculator used:

or

The result should be 9, 19, 29, 39, etc.

To set up a constant 'add 9' function beginning at 10, press the following keys, depending on the calculator used:

The result should be 19, 28, 37, 46.

To set up a constant minus function, use the minus sign (-) instead of the plus sign (+).

This activity develops children's understanding that the position of a digit signifies its value. It also offers an effective means of familiarising children with large numbers in a meaningful way.

Preparation

Copy photocopiable pages 108 to 110 for each child in the class. Check which method of setting up a constant function works with the calculators that are going to be used. For extension activity: make copies of photocopiable page 111.

Resources needed

For each child: copies of photocopiable sheets 108 to 110, writing materials and paper, a calculator. For extension activity: copies of photocopiable page 111.

What to do

Give each child a basic calculator. Explain how to programme the calculator to add in 10s. Ask them to press the following keys (or the correct keys for the type of calculator being used) in sequence:

Write this clearly on the board so that all the children can see it.

Ask the children what they notice when they continue to press (=) . Do they notice that the numbers jump forward in 10s? Can they see that the numbers are getting bigger and that they are going up in 10s?

Ask them to repeat the procedure from the beginning. Check that each child knows how to set up a constant 'add 10' function on the calculator. Repeat the procedure and check each calculator. Discuss what happens when they continue to press (=) after 100. Which digit is changing?

Ask the children to complete the 'add 10' dot-to-dot picture on photocopiable sheet 108 using the calculator.

Now ask the children to think of a way of adding in 100s instead of adding in 10s. Draw their attention to the procedure on the board, then from questioning and discussion, try to elicit from them the following procedure:

$$\boxed{1}\,\boxed{0}\,\boxed{0}\,\boxed{+}\,\boxed{+}\,\boxed{=}\,\boxed{=}\,\boxed{=}\,\boxed{=}$$

(or the correct method for the type of calculator being used) Allow some time to explore this procedure.

Ask questions such as:
▲ Which digit is changing as you press $\boxed{=}$?
▲ What is happening to the zeros?
▲ Are the numbers going up in 10s this time?
▲ How do we know these are bigger numbers?

Ask the children to work individually to write down in sequence all the numbers up to 1000 as they press $\boxed{=}$. When they have had a chance to do this, ask one child to call out the numbers and write them on the board as follows: 100, 200, 300, 400, 500, 600, 700, 800, 900, 1000.

Discuss what happens when you continue to press $\boxed{=}$ after 1000. Which digit is changing? Ask the children to complete the 'add 100' dot-to-dot picture on photocopiable sheet 109 using the calculator to help them.

Get the children to think about how they would add on 10s starting at 5. Allow some time to explore and discuss their ideas.

Ask them to press the following keys (or the correct keys for the type of calculator they are using):

$$\boxed{5}\,\boxed{+}\,\boxed{+}\,\boxed{1}\,\boxed{0}\,\boxed{=}\,\boxed{=}\,\boxed{=}\,\boxed{=}$$

The result should be 5, 15, 25, 35. Discuss with the children what is happening. (We are counting on in 10s from 5.) Distribute photocopiable page 110. Ask the children to complete the 'add 10' function dot-to-dot starting with 5, using the calculator to help them.

Let the children explore counting in 10s starting with other numbers. Ask them to make up their own sequences and write them down. Get them to then ask a friend to identify the constant used and continue the sequence.

Suggestion(s) for extension
Let the children decide on a constant on the calculator on their own and find a sequence of numbers. They can then write down the sequence on to the blank dot-to-dot picture on photocopiable page 111, and pass them to a friend who should try to work out what the constant is and complete the picture.

Ask them to explore what happens when they key in minus $\boxed{-}$ instead of $\boxed{+}$. What happens if they use a constant of 10 and begin on 20? What do they notice? Ask questions such as 'How many times did you press the $\boxed{=}$ key to reach 100?' Extend the discussion to the process of multiplication.

Suggestion(s) for support
Spend some time with the children counting in 2s, 3s and so on using a number line. Now distribute the calculators and use single-digit numbers.

100
200
300
400
500
600

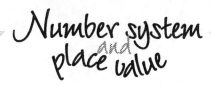

Teach the children how to get a constant of 2. Use questioning as in the main activity. For example, 'What is happening to the numbers as you continue to press $(=)$?'

Now move on to a constant of 10 and encourage children to explain what they are doing. Ask them to write down some of the numbers they are getting in sequence, e.g. 20, 30, 40, 50.

Assessment opportunities

Note whether all the children in the group have learned the skill of setting up a constant function on the calculator. Use questioning to determine whether all children recognise the effect of adding 10 and 100 to a number. Review their completed puzzle sheets as evidence of their performance and understanding.

Opportunities for IT

Children's use of calculators should be considered a part of their IT development. Setting up the constant function on the calculator will help them to appreciate the necessity for accurate keying and the following of a procedure. In actual fact the calculator models the tens number system and the children are creating a system which models the repeated addition or subtraction of a number.

Children should also be encouraged to look at their answers and check them for accuracy, relating the result to the expected answer and the keys pressed. As with computers themselves, calculators depend on accurate keying and the correct sequences of commands to create accurate results.

Reference to photocopiable sheets

Photocopiable pages 108 to 111 offer children dot-to-dot activities for the above task.

MONEY MONEY MONEY

To be able to convert prices to decimal notation.
†† *Whole class or large group then pairs.*
🕐 *30–40 minutes.*

Previous skills/knowledge needed

Children need previously to have been introduced to examples of the language of fractions in the context of some practical activities. They should have begun to appreciate place value.

Key background information

£ is the symbol for pound and is placed before the amount. p is the abbreviation for pence and is placed after the amount. £ and p should not appear together. The decimal point separates the pounds from the pence and there should always be two digits in the pence column.

Preparation

Copy photocopiable pages 112 and 113 directly on to card or mount copies on to card. If possible, laminate or cover the card with clear adhesive plastic film. Make copies for each child and cut out the individual cards. For the support activity make copies of page 114 for each child.

Resources needed

For each child: a set of picture cards, money cards and price tags cut from photocopiable sheets 112 and 113; paper and writing materials for support and extension activities. For support activity: copy of photocopiable page 114.

What to do

Give out the picture cards (cut from photocopiable page 112). Discuss the price of the various objects with the whole class. Talk about the notation and make children aware of the position of the decimal point, the pound sign and the pence sign.

Now distribute the money cards. Explain that you want the children to find different ways of expressing the different prices. For example, the price of the car, which is £1.50, can be stated as £1.50 or 150p. Ask the children to find the two cards which show these ways of stating the price. Place the three cards along in a line on the table (the toy car card, the money card showing £1.50 and the money card showing 150p).

Discuss what they have done: 'Do these prices mean the same amount or a different amount? What is the same as 150p?'

Ask the children to match the remaining money cards with the appropriate object. Ask questions as they work to ensure they understand the interchangeability of the terms.

Ask the children to work in pairs and explain that they are going to play a game similar to snap with the money cards. Stress that they are not looking for identical cards, but for cards of the same value, for example £3.20 and 320p.

Suggestion(s) for extension

Get the children to make up their own money stories, writing down the amounts in the two ways, for example:

My weekly pocket money is _____ _____
My savings are _____ _____
My favourite sweets cost _____ _____

Suggestions for support

Work with a small group and give further practice in converting the prices into decimal notation and back.

Use the examples on photocopiable page 114. Try to cut close to the line drawing. Help the children to make up more examples for themselves (using the blank card and writing on the reverse of the cards also) to give others in the group to complete.

Assessment opportunities

Were the children able to match the objects with the money cards? This constitutes evidence of their ability to convert prices from pence to decimal notation and vice versa. Make a note of how confident and speedy they were in carrying out the conversions. Did some individuals need much support from you or could they work independently?

Opportunities for IT

Children could word process their simple sentences about money stories. The text entry could be kept quite short and the exercise used to introduce children to the way of entering numbers and the £ sign on to the screen.

Display ideas

Get the children who needed extra support to colour their price tags on both sides. Help them to thread each tag on to string and hang it as a mobile in the classroom.

Reference to photocopiable sheets

Photocopiable pages 112 to 114 provide a set of priced objects, money cards and price tag cards. The money cards are used in the game of snap.

MULTIPLY BY 10 AND 100

To recognise the effect of multiplying by 1, 10 and 100.
†† *Pairs.*
🕐 *30 minutes.*

Previous skills/knowledge needed

Children need to have had previous experience of multiplying by single-digit numbers and counting in 2s, 3s, 4s and so on to 10.

Preparation

Prepare a copy of the recording sheet on photocopiable page 115.

Resources needed

Photocopiable page 115 (a recording sheet for each pair), a calculator for each pair, three dice per pair.

What to do

Provide each pair of children with a dice and a calculator, and give each child a recording sheet (from photocopiable page 115).

Explain to the children that the purpose of the activity is to explore what happens when we multiply numbers by 1, 10 and 100. First discuss what they think will happen. Introduce the photocopiable sheet. Ask the children to press the ③ button on the calculator then multiply by one. Discuss what happens.

Repeat the process, this time multiplying by 10. What happens this time? Ask the children to throw the dice to obtain a different number. Complete the calculator operation again. Ask questions such as: 'What happened? Why?'

Ask one child in each pair to throw the dice and to multiply that number by 1. Discuss what happens. Repeat the process but this time multiply the number by 10. Discuss the outcome with the children. Point out that the first digit is still there but

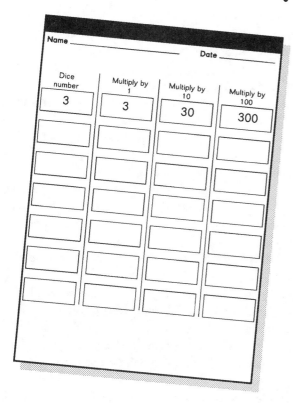

Name _____ Date _____			
Dice number	Multiply by 1	Multiply by 10	Multiply by 100
3	3	30	300

it now has zero after it. Explain that it is in a different position which means 10s.

Establish that, regardless of the number you start with, it will end in zero if you multiply by 10, and remain the same when you multiply by 1. Help the children to record their results in the first two columns of the recording sheet. Ask them to throw the dice again and multiply by 1 and then by 10 and record their result as before. Repeat the procedure.

Now give each pair a second dice. Ask them to throw two dice, add the result and multiply it by 10. They should record their result on their recording sheet as before. Once again discuss what has happened. Draw the children's attention to the fact that multiplying by 10 always results in the last digit being zero and the original digits remaining in the answer, but changing position. They should continue throwing two dice, adding the result, multiplying this by 1 and 10 and recording the final number on the sheet, until the first two columns are completed.

Next ask the children to go back to the first number they got when they threw the single dice, and multiply this number by 100. Ask them to discuss what they notice. Encourage them to appreciate that the digits they key in to the calculator remain in the answer but shift position and that there are two zeros to the right of these digits.

Ask them to compare this result with the result they got when they multiplied the same number by 1 and by 10.

Encourage them to realise that this answer is far bigger, and that in fact it is 10 times bigger. Help them to multiply each number (listed in the first column of the recording sheet) by 100. They should compare the results as they go along. Help them to appreciate how this number has an extra zero

which makes it 10 times bigger than the number in the previous column.

Suggestion(s) for extension
Encourage these children to devise a new recording sheet based on throwing three dice, and including multiplying by other numbers as well as 10, 100 and 1.

Suggestion(s) for support
Some children will need to work with apparatus to support them. Ask them to sort interlocking cubes into some sets of 10 and explain that they should exchange every one cube for 10 cubes. Also use a simple function machine to help the children see what is happening.

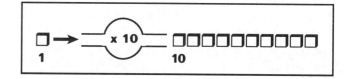

Ask the children to choose a number between 3 and 9 and then take that number of single cubes. Ask them to exchange each cube for a set of 10. Only when the children have played this exchange game should you ask them to try out the same operation using a calculator and discuss what happens when they multiply by 10 and later by 100, using the calculator.

Assessment opportunities

Check the children's responses to your questioning. Note their ability to read the numbers on the calculator display. Can they explain the effect of multiplying by 1, 10 and 100?

Are they able to explain the fact that the digits remain the same but have shifted, thus changing the value of the number.

3   30

multiply by 10

Display ideas

Make a function machine called the 'multiply by 10' machine using a large cardboard box and display it with a number of cubes, and number cards so that it can be used as an interactive display as well as a future resource.

Reference to photocopiable sheets

Photocopiable page 115 can be used for recording the results in the main activity. The first row of the photocopiable sheet has been completed.

EQUAL PARTS

To begin to recognise that a whole can be partitioned into equal parts; to recognise halves and quarters of a whole.

✝✝ *Large group or whole class.*

🕐 *30 minutes.*

Previous skills/knowledge needed

The children should appreciate cardinality and conservation, i.e. they should be able to identify sets with the same number of objects and recognise that the number in the set remains the same regardless of the arrangement of the objects.

Key background information

In the early stages of work on fractions, it is essential that children should associate a fraction with a specific object, for example, a half of a piece of string. Therefore, you should refer to the whole to which a half applies. There is a danger if they use the symbol ($\frac{1}{2}$) alone children may think that all halves are equal to each other. Therefore, the emphasis of this activity is placed on the language of fraction work and no formal notation for fractions is introduced at this stage.

Preparation

Collect a range of objects which can be partitioned into parts. Arrange the classroom so that everyone can hear and see what you are doing.

Resources needed

An apple, a sharp knife, sheets of paper, lengths of string, Plasticine or modelling clay.

What to do

Ask the children to think of how they could share the apple with a friend so that each person gets a piece which is the same size. Encourage them to use the language of fractions (halving, cut it into two parts so they are both the same size, cut it into two equal parts, and so on).

Slice the apple in two. Discuss what you have done, using questions and statements: 'How many parts have I made? We have two equal parts. We have divided the apple into two equal parts. We have halved the apple. We have cut it in halves. How many halves? Are the two parts the same size? Look at them carefully. We can cut an apple into two halves and each part is the same size. My friend gets an equal share of my apple because I divided it in halves. Two of us share the apple equally.'

Lift up one half and ask, 'Is this a whole apple? How would I get a whole apple back again?' Put the two halves together to demonstrate that the whole apple is made up of two halves.

Ask the children to think of other food which they could halve in order to share with a friend (an orange, a bar of chocolate, a biscuit, a bun and so on). Discuss how they can divide each one into two equal parts and how each equal part is a half.

Now consider the other objects: the piece of string, the lump of Plasticine and the sheet of paper. Take each one in

turn and ask the children to say how they could be divided into two parts so that each part is the same size. Encourage the kind of interaction described above.

Next say to the children that you might like to share your apple between four people instead of two. Discuss how they would do this. Explain how every person must get an equal part. This will involve using the following language: half, halves, halving, quarter, quarters, quartering and whole.

Ask the children to think about ways of sharing a sheet of paper between four people so that each person gets an equal part. Try to elicit the following sort of talk: 'First I divide the page into two parts.' Demonstrate how to fold a page to obtain halves and fold again to obtain quarters. 'Now the whole page has been divided into two halves. Next I can divide each part again, being careful to divide them equally so that each one is the same size. Now I have four parts. All the parts are the same size. I have four quarters.'

Continue discussing and questioning in this way to ensure the children hear and use the language of fractions.

Suggestion(s) for extension

Encourage the children to realise that a half is made up of two quarters. Extend the discussion as follows: 'How many halves in the whole apple? Let's count how many we made. How many quarters in the whole apple? Let's count how many we made. Would two quarters make a whole? Can you tell me why not? Two quarters is the same as a half and this is less than a whole. The two quarters look the same size as the half. There are two quarters in a half.'

Throughout the discussion use the objects to demonstrate.

Suggestion(s) for support

Give the children further opportunities to handle the halves you have made and to see that the object or the whole has been partitioned into parts of equal size.

Encourage them to list other things which could be divided into two equal parts.

Give them practice in partitioning whole objects, such as Plasticine, a cucumber, a tomato, a bar of chocolate and so on, combined with lots of opportunities to talk about what they are doing.

Assessment opportunities

Because this activity involves whole class or large group discussion, the main source of evidence for assessment is what the children say and how they respond to your questions. For this reason, it will probably be more appropriate to decide in advance of the lesson which children you wish to focus on for assessment purposes. At the end of the session, on the basis of their contributions, consider whether these children can recognise halves and quarters of a whole and have grasped the fact that a whole can be divided into equal parts.

MATCHING HALVES

To recognise halves of a whole.

†† *Pairs.*

🕑 *20–30 minutes.*

Previous skills/knowledge needed

Children need to have been introduced to some of the language of fractions in the context of practical activities. They should appreciate the notion of partitioning a whole into parts.

Key background information

Symmetry is an effective way of promoting fraction concepts. An axis of symmetry divides a shape into two halves. If a shape has exactly two axes of symmetry, those axes divide the shape into four quarters.

Preparation

Copy photocopiable page 116 directly on to card twice or mount copies on to card. Make two copies for each pair. If possible, laminate or cover the cards with clear adhesive plastic film. Cut out the shapes.

Arrange the children so they can work in pairs, and give each pair a set of symmetry shapes.

Resources needed

For each pair: set of symmetry shapes cut from photocopiable page 116.

What to do

Distribute a set of symmetry shapes to each pair. Ask them to spread the shapes out on the table in front of them. Ask one child to lift up a shape. Explain that it is, for example, a part of a whole circle. Invite the children to search for another equal part to match it in order to make a whole circle. Encourage the children to say what they have done. Ask questions such as the following: 'How many parts make up the whole circle? Show me a half of the whole. How many halves are in a whole? Are both these parts the same size?' and so on.

Select two parts which do not match. Ask, 'Can I match these two parts to make a whole object?' Encourage the children to say that the parts must be equal in size.

Ask the children to match all the pairs. Encourage the use of the language of fractions as they work.

When all the halves are matched, get the children to swap partners and discuss what shapes they completed and how they knew which ones were correct. At the end of the activity, summarise what the children did by emphasising that there are two halves in a whole, that the halves are equal in size and that a whole can be divided into two equal parts.

Suggestion(s) for extension
Encourage pairs of children to draw and cut out their own symmetrical shapes for their friends to match.

Suggestion(s) for support
Watch out for children who are finding it difficult to match the shapes. Do they understand that the two parts must be equal? Do they understand the meaning of 'equal'? Spend some time working with them and verbalising what they are doing when they match the shapes.

Assessment opportunities
If the children can match the shapes confidently and fairly quickly and if they can also tell you that they need two halves or two equal parts to make a whole, this offers evidence of their ability to recognise halves of a whole.

Reference to photocopiable sheets
Photocopiable page 116 provides a set of halves which can be matched to make whole shapes.

PARTITIONING SETS
To begin to recognise that sets can be partitioned into equal parts; to be able to partition sets up to 12 into two or four equal parts.
†† *Pairs.*
🕐 *30 minutes.*

Previous skills/knowledge needed
Children should be familiar with the language of fractions: halving, halves, equal parts, whole, quarters and quartering.

Preparation
Collect a range of objects which can be partitioned into two and four sets of equal number (for example, beads or counters). Arrange the classroom so children can work in pairs.

Resources needed
For each pair: small objects such as Unifix cubes, beads or counters, paper and writing materials.

What to do
Begin by discussing previous work the children have done on fractions: halving shapes, matching shapes and so on (for example the previous two activities).

Give each pair a set of six objects and ask them to divide it into two groups with the same number of objects in each group. Discuss with the children the fact that each group contains the same number of objects and, when put together, they make the full set of six objects. Point out how each group is half of the set of six objects.

Help the children to record on paper what they have done. Encourage them to begin by drawing a diagram as follows:

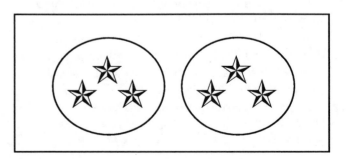

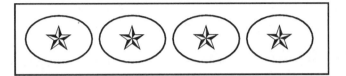

They should then write under the diagram: 'One half of 6 is 3.'

Repeat this activity using even numbers to 12. Encourage them to draw another diagram and write similar statements to explain what they have done for 8, 10 and 12 objects.

Then challenge the children to divide a set of 4 objects into four equal groups and to record on paper what they

have done. Let them go on to partition eight and twelve objects into four equal groups. Each time encourage the children to record what they have done using a diagram and writing a statement.

Suggestion(s) for extension

Discuss the problem of partitioning into two groups sets that contain an odd number of elements. (Is it possible to give each member the same number of objects and still use up all the objects in the set?) Help them to realise that you must have an even number in the set to share the objects into two equal parts.

Ask them to investigate whether this is also the case for sharing objects into four equal parts. Get them to try to reach a conclusion by experimenting with different numbers (up to twelve) in the set. What about three equal parts?

Suggestion(s) for support

Ask the children to work in pairs and divide the sets into two equal groups. Explain that they should each take an equal number of objects.

Question them as follows: 'How many cubes have you? How many has your partner? How many make up the whole set? How much of the set did each person get?' Help the children to remake the set and then break it into equal parts again.

Ask one member of the pair to record the result on a diagram while the other writes the statement underneath.

To partition larger sets of objects into four groups, for example 12, invite the children to work with another pair. Again, ask them to share out the objects in the set between them so that each member of the group gets the same

number. Question them about how many they now have, whether they have the same number each, how many are in the whole set, etc. Encourage them to recognise that they each have a quarter of the set. One member of the group should record the result on a diagram while another writes the statement underneath.

Assessment opportunities

Ask the children to show you their diagrams recording what they did. Discuss their diagrams with them: 'What does this mean? How many groups did you make? How much of the set is here?' pointing to one partition of the set, and so on.

Establish from their diagrams and their responses whether they have grasped which sets (up to 12) can be divided into two, three or four equal parts.

SHARING BETWEEN THREE

To begin to appreciate the need for a range of fractions, specifically, to appreciate that halves and quarters are inadequate for partitioning some sets; to begin to become aware of the need for the fraction one-third.
†† *Groups of three, then large group or whole class.*
🕐 *30–40 minutes.*

Previous skills/knowledge needed

Children should be familiar with some fraction language, for example, halving, quartering, halves and quarters, and so on. They should understand the process of halving and quartering and know that there are two halves in a whole and four quarters in a whole.

Preparation

Collect a selection of objects, some of which can be partitioned into three equal parts (for example, rectangular biscuits), and some of which cannot be partitioned into equal parts easily, for example, circular sandwich biscuits. Arrange the classroom so that everyone can hear what you are saying and see what you are doing.

Copy photocopiable page 117 directly on to card or mount copies on to card. Colour the cards if possible and then laminate them or cover them with clear adhesive plastic film. Each group of three children should have access to several copies, if necessary.

Resources needed
Paper and writing materials, a variety of biscuits such as rectangular plain biscuits and circular biscuits with a jam centre, copies of the biscuit shapes from photocopiable page 117.

What to do
Begin the lesson by reminding the children of previous work involving fractions. Remind them of the conclusions they drew, for example, that if you share biscuits equally between two people, each person gets a half of the biscuits. If you share biscuits equally between four people, each person gets a quarter of the biscuits. If necessary, demonstrate these conclusions using counting materials such as beads or counters.

Distribute one rectangular biscuit to each group of three children. Discuss how it might be cut or broken to give each child an equal share. Demonstrate by drawing a diagram on the board and marking where you would break the biscuit to make three equal bits. Explain how each bit can be called one-third.

Distribute two biscuits to each group of three. Ask them how they would share the two biscuits equally between them. Make sure they know that 'equally' means that everyone must get the same amount. Encourage the children to offer a response and to experiment. Question them as follows: 'Would halving them be a good idea if you want three people to have equal parts? Why not? Would quartering be a good idea if you want three people to have equal parts? Why not?'

Help them to come to the conclusion that the best plan would be to divide each biscuit into three parts, i.e. into thirds.

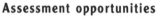

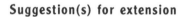

Help them to understand that each person would then get one-third of each biscuit, and that they would each get two of the thirds which would make two-thirds.

Finally, give each child a copy of photocopiable page 117. Ask the children to work individually and mark the biscuits to show the best way of cutting them into three equal parts. When they have completed this, discuss the results with them. Discuss how some biscuits, for example, circular ones with jam in the middle, are more difficult to divide.

Suggestion(s) for extension
Ask the children to investigate sharing four biscuits between three children.

Suggestion(s) for support
Let the children work in pairs and then groups of four so that they only need to share the biscuits between two and then four children.

Assessment opportunities
Question individual children on what they did. Check whether they understand the concept of one-third and that there are three thirds in the whole. The problem-solving task involving the sharing of two biscuits between three children may offer interesting insights into the children's thinking: what strategies are they applying?

Reference to photocopiable sheets
Photocopiable page 117 provides shapes for children to mark into thirds.

FINDING MORE FRACTIONS

To begin to recognise different ways of representing the same amount using different fractions and fractions of different sets.

†† *Pairs*

🕐 *30–40 minutes.*

Previous skills/knowledge needed

Children need to have been introduced to some of the language of fractions in the context of practical activities. They should appreciate the notion of partitioning a whole into halves and quarters. They should also be able to partition sets of different numbers (up to 12) into equal parts.

Preparation

Copy photocopiable page 118 directly on to card or mount copies on to card. If possible, laminate or cover the card with clear adhesive plastic film. Make one set for each pair. Cut out the sets.

For the support activity, copy photocopiable page 119 directly on to card or mount copies on to card. If possible, laminate or cover the card with clear adhesive plastic film. Make copies for each pair and cut out the fractions which will be used in the construction of a 'fraction families board'.

Resources needed

For each pair: a set of fraction cards and number cards cut from photocopiable page 118, Unifix cubes or similar, paper and writing materials. For support activity: copy of photocopiable page 119.

What to do

Arrange the children in pairs. Give each pair a box of cubes. Distribute a set of fraction cards and numbers to each pair. Place the fraction cards in a pile in the corner of the table. Work with the children as they complete the following tasks:

▲ Ask them to divide a set of eight cubes into two groups so that each group has the same number. Get them to discuss what they have done using the following type of questioning: 'How many cubes are in each group? Tell me what you did. Did you halve the set of eight?' Now ask them to look for the fraction and number cards which say what they have done. They should find the cards which show $\frac{1}{2}$ of 8 and 4. Check that each pair has selected the correct statement. Ask them to place this statement on one side of the table and return the cubes to the box.

▲ Ask them to divide a set of 16 cubes into four groups so that each group has the same number. Help them to discuss what they have done asking the following type of questions: 'How many cubes are there in each group? Tell me what you did. Did you halve the set of 16? Did you quarter the set of 16? How many groups did you make?' Now ask them to look for the fraction and number cards which say what they have done. They should select the cards which show $\frac{1}{4}$ of 16 and 4. Check that each pair has selected the correct statement. Ask them to place this on one side of the table and return the cubes to the box.

▲ Ask them to divide a set of eight

---

cubes into four groups so that each group has the same number. Get them to discuss what they have done asking the following type of questioning: 'Did you divide the set equally? How many cubes are there in each group? Tell me what you did. Did you quarter the set of eight? How many groups did you make?' Now ask them to look for the fraction and number cards which say what they have done. They should find the cards which show $\frac{1}{4}$ of 8 and 2. Check that each pair has chosen the correct statement. Ask them to place it to one side and return the cubes to the box.

▲ Ask them to divide a set of 16 cubes into two groups so each group has the same number. Get them to discuss what they have done, asking questions as above. Once again ask them to use the cards to make a statement about what they have done. Read the statement with them and relate it to the partitioning. Return the cubes to the box once more.

▲ Finally, ask them to divide a set of 32 cubes into four groups so that each group has the same number. Get them to discuss what they have done asking questions as above. Invite them to make a statement using the cards. Return the cubes to the box.

Now ask the children to examine the statements they have made. Ask questions and encourage responses such as: 'What do you notice about some of the statements? They have the same answer. Which ones have the same answer? So half of 8 is the same as a quarter of 16.'

Challenge the children to make further statements of this kind. Allow time for the children to discuss the statements among themselves in pairs.

Praise them for being so observant and explain to them that they are now going to play a game similar to snap, but instead of looking for identical cards, they should look for matching number and fraction cards. Thus $\frac{1}{2}$ of 8 can be 'snapped' with 4. Collect all the cards, remove the = cards and shuffle the remainder. Then let the children play the game in pairs. When necessary, let them check their responses by taking out the relevant set of cubes and partitioning it.

Suggestion(s) for extension
Encourage the children to make up their own fraction statements, using cubes to help them if necessary.

Suggestion(s) for support
Get the children to build a fraction families board using photocopiable page 119. Explain that they should colour the members of the half family red; the quarter family blue; the sixth family green and the eighth family yellow. Encourage lots of discussion about the work, including comments about equivalence, for example, 'What other fractions are the same as one half? How do you know?'

Assessment opportunities
Check whether individuals completed the partitioning tasks accurately. Make a note of how confident and speedy they were in carrying them out. Did some individuals need much support from you or could they work independently? Were the children beginning to recognise different ways of representing the same amount using different fractions? The evidence for this will come mainly from the discussion of the statements following these tasks but will also come from the partitioning tasks themselves.

Display ideas
Get the children who did the support activity to write out the names of their own fraction families and to display them as they are or stick them on to suitably-sized sheets of sugar paper for a class book entitled 'Fraction families'.

Reference to photocopiable sheets
Photocopiable page 118 provides a set of fraction, whole number and = cards which can be used for making fraction statements. The fraction and number cards are also used in the game of 'snap'. Photocopiable page 119 contains fractions which can be used with those needing extra support to build fraction families.

Number relationships

Developing an understanding of number includes recognising the relationship between numbers and developing effective strategies for computation. The programme of study for number contains specific references to both these aspects and this chapter contains activities which aim to promote this understanding. Three inter-related aspects are addressed in turn, namely, patterns, number facts and special numbers.

The ability to spot pattern is among the key factors in our efficiency as learners. It helps us to organise and sort out our experiences and to deal with the complexity of the world. In essence, it enables us to predict events. Mathematics can be considered to be a search for pattern and order. The number system, in particular, is based upon pattern. The activities on number pattern are designed to encourage children to explore numbers and to reflect on their own strategies, as opposed to being initiated into a series of rules, steps and procedures.

NUMBER

INVESTIGATING PATTERN

Pattern is not necessarily an end in itself. When looking for patterns in number children are searching for predictable sequences. Predictable sequences and configurations assist them in coming to grips with the structure of the number system and in committing to memory important number facts. The activities based on number facts are designed to help children acquire some number facts and to calculate quickly and accurately. The rest of the activities are intended to support the development of concepts of numbers that can often pose particular difficulties, for example, zero: it is important to note that the notion of an empty set is abstract, that while children may have little or no difficulty grasping the concept of a physical collection of objects, they may not understand the possibility of *nothing* and the number zero corresponding to *nothing*. Children need to see zero as a number rather than a symbol for the absence of a number.

All the activities in this section are designed in such a way as to promote discussion and thinking for oneself. Talk, especially talk which encourages pupils to ask questions, helps with the consolidation of mathematical facts and with seeing the relationship between facts. Discussion allows you to gain an insight into the thinking of learners and then determine whether they really understand an idea or whether their thinking is muddled. Many of the activities also include recording sheets which help to provide further evidence of the children's learning.

Key background information

The ability to recognise pattern is among the key factors in our efficiency as learners. It helps us to organise and sort out our experiences and deal with the complexity of the world. In essence, it enables us to predict events. Mathematics can be considered to be a search for pattern and order. The number system, in particular, is based upon pattern, but before children can begin to notice patterns in numbers they need to be given opportunities to notice patterns on real objects.

Preparation

Collect about ten artefacts with patterns for example, toys, wallpaper, wrapping paper, lace, patterned ribbon, fabric, ceramics etc.

Prepare for the follow-up activities by making a list of lots of nursery rhymes.

Resources needed

A collection of patterned artefacts, a tray, paint, potato cuts, paper.

What to do

Place various objects on a tray on the table and direct the children's attention towards the patterns on the objects.

Invite each child in turn to take an object from the tray and say something about it.

Encourage the children to listen carefully to what each other says.

Ask the children to exchange their object with the person next to them and encourage them to try to remember what was said about it. Give each child the chance to repeat what their partner said about the artefact. Next encourage the children to look closely at the object they are now holding and to describe it. Help the children with their descriptions by asking them questions which focus their attention on the pattern, for example 'What colours do you notice? Is there more than one colour? What can you say about the shape? How would you describe the design?' If necessary, draw the children's attention to the patterns on the artefacts, for example, 'This toy car has a green stripe along both sides. This watch strap has white and yellow dots on a black background.'

Ask them to close their eyes and try to picture the pattern in their heads and describe it out loud.

Ask a child to think of one of the artefacts without telling the others which one she has chosen. Encourage the others

SPOT THE PATTERN

To be able to recognise and describe patterns on objects.

†† *Group of six.*

🕓 *30–40 minutes.*

Previous skills/knowledge needed

Children should be able to do tasks involving one-to-one correspondence. They should also be able to use the language of ordinal number correctly.

to work out which one it is by asking questions about its shape, colour, design, pattern and so on. At this stage it is important to allow lots of discussion, observation and description of the objects.

Follow this activity by asking the children to clap out simple rhythms in music and to say lots of nursery rhymes together. Encourage the children to notice the rhyming words and pick them out. The children can also paint repeating patterns, for example by using potato cuts, and explore movement patterns in PE.

Suggestion(s) for extension

Encourage the children to make a sound pattern by clapping, then think about a way of recording it so they could make the pattern another time. Discuss the best way of recording (marks on a page, numbers, etc). Get them to look at the repeating patterns other children have made, for example in art, and describe them using numbers.

Suggestion(s) for support

The key to recognising patterns is close observation. Spend time with the children and give them lots of opportunities to notice and describe the patterns. For example, encourage them to say what they are going to do in the art activity, and then to put into language what they have done.

Assessment opportunities

Observe individual children as they describe their artefacts. Do they do this accurately? Do they have the necessary language? Note which children, if any, need further practice in describing patterns. Note their use of language in describing their own patterns. Do they use this language appropriately and confidently?

Opportunities for IT

Children could use an art or graphics package to make their own patterns. This activity could be used to introduce children to making shapes and filling them with colours. Some children might be able to copy the shapes they have made to create enough identical objects to repeat the pattern.

Framework software like *My World* can be set up so that children can drag a range of predetermined objects on to the screen to make a simple pattern. A partner could then try to make the same pattern underneath the first. The activity is an interesting way to reinforce work on simple pattern and to introduce children to using a mouse to drag objects around the screen. The resulting patterns could be printed out and used for a class display.

Display ideas

Mount children's art work under the caption 'Patterns we have made'. The children could then make a three-colour pattern or use some of the patterned materials to make a collage.

DRESS THE TEDDY

To be able to recognise and describe a sequence of events; to be able to predict the next stage in a sequence.

†† *Large group discussion, then working in pairs.*

🕐 *30–40 minutes.*

Previous skills/knowledge needed

Children should be able to do tasks involving one-to-one correspondence and be able to use the language of ordinal number correctly.

Preparation

Use photocopiable page 120 to prepare a set of teddy cards for each child. If possible colour these and then laminate them or cover in clear adhesive plastic.

Resources needed

For each child: set of teddy cards cut from photocopiable sheet 120, paper, pencils, crayons and felt-tipped pens, scissors.

What to do

Introduce the activity by talking with the children about getting dressed for school in the morning. What do they put on first? What next? What do they put on last? Which goes on first – their coat or their jumper?

Extend the discussion to sequence events in the school day. Discuss the day's plan. (What will we do after break? What is going to happen when we come back after dinner?)

Dress the teddy

Now distribute a set of teddy cards to each child. Ask the children to sort the cards into the order in which teddy puts his clothes on each morning. Once they have sequenced the cards, ask them to say what they have done. Question individual children about the sequence they have made.

Ask the children each to look at another child's sequence. Ask questions, such as: 'Are they both the same? Did you make up a different story? What is the difference?'

Ask each child to join with a partner and turn one set of cards upside down on the table, but keeping the same sequence. One child should then turn over the first three cards and the other child must try to predict the next (fourth) card. The other child predicts the fifth and so on until the last card has been turned over. Now ask one child in each pair to make the sequence again but to leave out one or two cards. Explain that the partner should identify the missing cards.

Then ask the children to work in pairs with one set of cards, and take turns to describe a pattern for the other child to make.

Finally, get the children to make their own sequence cards. Explain that they should draw and colour a sequence of pictures showing the building up of a pattern, for example, dressing the snowman, laying one place at the table at dinner time and so on. Help them to cut out the cards and share them with a friend using any of the above ideas.

Suggestion(s) for extension

Ask the children to start at the end of the sequence and work back to the beginning. They could do some of the activities described above in doing this.

Suggestion(s) for support

Begin by using only two or three cards to introduce the idea of a pattern or a sequence and to provide lots of opportunities to use the relevant language. Ask questions such as: 'What happened first? What happened next? What happened last?'

Work through the tasks in the main activity using only two or three cards, for example, predicting the third card, identifying the missing card, and sorting the shuffled cards.

Extend the number of cards as appropriate. Encourage the children to say what they are doing as they build the patterns and to say what is new in each step of the pattern.

Get them to use the cards to make sequences for their partner to describe and have the partner describe a sequence for them to make.

Assessment opportunities

Observe individual children as they make the patterns. Have they grasped the idea of a sequence of events and have they understood the key language involved (before, after, next, last, first)? Can they describe what they have done using this language? Do they do this confidently? Are they able to predict the next step in the sequence or identify the missing step? Note which children, if any, need further practice in making and describing picture sequences.

Opportunities for IT

Framework software like *My World* can be set up to stimulate the dressing teddy sequencing. The results can be printed out for display.

More able children could use a word processor to type in and print the sequence. Younger children could use a concept keyboard linked to the word processor. The overlay could be set up either with the text sentences of the sequence (First you put on teddy's vest etc) or with pictures of the various clothes so that pressing the vest puts the sequence on to the screen.

More sophisticated computers and concept keyboards can be set up to include the pictures on the screen.

Display ideas

Make large cut-out teddies that the children can dress using fabric scraps and display them in a sequence.

Reference to photocopiable sheets

Photocopiable page 120 offers children a set of cards which can be sorted to build up a pattern.

NUMBER ARRAYS

To be able to recognise numbers from 1 to 10 placed in a variety of arrays; to be able to place up to 10 counters in systematic spatial patterns.

†† *Whole class, then pairs.*

🕐 *40–60 minutes.*

Previous skills/knowledge needed

Children should be able to undertake tasks involving one-to-one correspondence and be able to use the language of ordinal number correctly. They should be able to recognise and describe patterns.

Key background information

Pattern is not necessarily an end in itself. When looking for patterns in number, children are searching for predictable sequences and configurations they recognise. Such predictable sequences and configurations assist them in coming to grips with the structure of our number system and in committing to memory important number facts.

Preparation

Collect together lots of counting materials, for example beads, counters or Unifix cubes. Prepare a large sheet of card with the title 'Our number patterns' and numbers from 3 to 6 written down one side. Stick this in a prominent place where all the children will be able to see it. Make copies of photocopiable pages 121 and 122 for each pair and cut out the cards.

Resources needed

A bag or tray containing beads, counters or Unifix cubes, one large sheet of card and markers for recording, pencil, paper, coloured felt-tipped pens. For each pair: set of domino cards cut from photocopiable sheets 121 and 122.

What to do

Pass the bag or tray of counting materials to each child in turn and ask them each to take three counters and make a pattern with them. How many different ways can they arrange the counters to make a pattern of three? Help the children to describe what they have done through questioning, for example, is a straight line the only way to make a pattern using three counters? What has your friend done?

Encourage them to notice how the pattern changes according to where they are positioned at the time. For example, if they stand in front of the table, can they see a different pattern?

Go around the group or the class and record the different patterns that the children have made. Represent the patterns on the large sheet of card and discuss them with the class, helping get the children to describe their patterns so that you can record them on the chart.

Now ask each child to take four counters and to experiment with them to see how many different ways they can be arranged. Once again invite the children to look at the patterns their friends have made. Again, encourage the children to describe their patterns and record a selection of them on the chart. Do the same with five and six. Again, record some of the patterns on the chart.

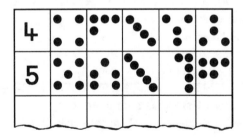

Encourage the children to continue on their own building up patterns to ten. Ask them to record on paper two ways of arranging the counters to make each number. Get them to compare their recorded arrangements with those of a partner.

Now distribute a set of number cards prepared from photocopiable sheet 121 to each pair of children. Let the children make up their own arrangements for each number. Encourage them to use the counters, if they wish, to help them to find the most interesting pattern. Get them to compare their number patterns with those of other pairs, discussing the similarities and differences.

Now give each child a set of dot cards prepared from photocopiable sheet 122. Ask the children to compare these patterns with their own and to match the two sets of cards beginning with 1.

Finally, the children can shuffle the two sets of cards and play snap.

Suggestion(s) for extension

When describing their patterns, draw the children's attention to the addition and multiplication facts which the patterns show. For example, in the case of six, the interpretation could be '3 sets of 2 is 6' or '3 sets of 2 is 6'.

Some pairs of children may also like to join with another pair, and share their dot cards so that they can consider number patterns greater than 10.

Assessment opportunities

Observe individual children as they prepare their number patterns using the counters. Do they do this confidently? Note which children, if any, have difficulty in recognising the arrays. Do they recognise number arrays to six? To ten? Do some children need more experience of this sort of activity? Note how accurately they match the dominoes. Are they becoming more familiar with the spatial patterns?

Reference to photocopiable sheets

Photocopiable pages 121 and 122 offer children sets of number and dot domino cards which can be sorted in various ways.

can be added together to make 6. Tell them that they can use the counters to assist them. Ask them to record their results. Encourage them to notice any patterns as they record the results, for example:

5 + 1 = 6; 4 + 2 = 6; 3 + 3 = 6; 2 + 4 = 6; 1 + 5 = 6

Help them to discuss the patterns by asking questions, for example:

▲ What do you notice about the numbers in your first column?

▲ What do you notice about the numbers after the + sign?

Encourage them to realise by organising their sums into a pattern, someone else could easily continue it for them. Can they make another pattern? Ask them what they notice about it.

Now ask the children to make 6 by adding three numbers together, for example 1 + 2 + 3 = 6. Encourage them to use the counters again to experiment. Get them to record their results on paper. Ask questions to help them notice the patterns, for example: How are the patterns different from the two-number additions? Are there are other patterns?

Let them explore other numbers up to 10 in the same way, i.e. by adding first two numbers and then three numbers together. Again, make sure that the children record their patterns each time and let them use the counters to help them if they wish.

BUILDING UP NUMBERS

To be able to partition a number; to be able to order addition sums in a systematic way; to begin to recognise the value of pattern in completing addition calculations.

†† *Group of four.*

⏱ *30–40 minutes.*

Previous skills/knowledge needed

Children should be able to complete tasks involving one-to-one correspondence and be able to use the language of ordinal number correctly. They should understand the addition of numbers to ten.

Preparation

Arrange for children to work in groups of four.

Resources needed

A bag or tray of beads, counters or Unifix cubes for each group, one large sheet of card and markers for recording, pencil and paper.

What to do

Give a bag or tray of counting materials to each group to be used in the activity if necessary. Explain to the children that you want them to think of different pairs of numbers that

Finally, ask the children to work in pairs and begin a pattern for another pair to complete. Discuss why it is easy to complete the pattern.

Suggestion(s) for extension

Challenge the children to build up larger numbers, for example 10, 11 or 12 by adding two and three digits. Ask them to make other patterns and to describe the pattern to a friend. Get them to record their results in a systematic way, as above. Ask them to start building up harder number patterns for their friends to continue.

Suggestion(s) for support

Partition numbers into 2 sets or explore ways to add two digits together to make numbers from, say, six to ten. Use digit cards for the children to record. Draw attention to the number facts which they have made.

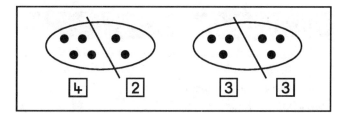

Assessment opportunities

Observe individual children as they build up the numbers. Note whether children are able to do this without the assistance of counters. On the basis of their recording, decide whether they can order addition sums in a systematic way. Ask the children to describe their patterns and to say how knowing the pattern helps them to complete a sequence.

Display ideas

Make a book of different number patterns for members of the class to complete.

SUBTRACTION PATTERNS

To be able to find several subtraction calculations that have the same answer; to recognise patterns in subtraction calculations; to be able to order subtraction sums in a systematic way.

†† *Whole class with some individual work.*

🕑 *30–40 minutes.*

Previous skills/knowledge needed

Children should be able to subtract numbers within 20.

Preparation

Make copies on card of the recording sheet on page 123 for each child.

Ensure that the children have enough work space for the

individual task: they will need to be able to write on the recording sheets, as well as use beads, counters or Unifix cubes.

Resources needed

Beads, counters or Unifix cubes, a large sheet of card, markers, pencils, recording sheets (from photocopiable page 123).

What to do

Ask the children to use the beads, counters or Unifix cubes to see how many subtraction sums they can make using any of the numbers 1 to 20 for which the answer is 2. Discuss some examples as a whole class before asking children to work individually. Record some of the results on a chart or on the board. (Allow children to use counters if they wish.)

When the children have found lots of sums, encourage them to discuss what they have done. Ask them to look carefully at their sums and see if they can be arranged in a special order for example:

20 – 18	or 20 – 18	or 19 – 17
19 – 17	18 – 16	17 – 15
18 – 16	14 – 12	15 – 13
17 – 15	12 – 10	and so on.
and so on	and so on	

Help the children to discuss the system or the pattern through questioning. What do they notice about the list of sums? What do they notice about all the numbers on the left

pattern. Do they understand the idea of building up a pattern and how the pattern shows what the next sum should be? Check this through questioning, covering all sums except the first two, and then asking them to predict what the next sum should be. Note to what extent individual children are able to do this without support from you. On the basis of this, decide whether they can order subtraction sums in a systematic way.

Display ideas
Make a chart recording some of the children's subtraction patterns.

Reference to photocopiable sheets
Photocopiable page 123 provides a recording sheet for the results of this activity.

NUMBER GRIDS

To recognise patterns of multiples up to 5 × 5 and later 10 × 10. To be able to use patterns of multiples to help solve multiplication sums.

†† *Small group work followed by individual investigation.*

🕑 *30–40 minutes.*

as they go down? What happens to all the numbers after the subtraction sign? If they only had the first two sums, could they finish off the pattern easily? How?

Ask the children to record their patterns on the recording sheet, then share them through a whole-class discussion. Finally, ask individual children to describe the start of their pattern and invite the rest of the class to say what the next sum will be.

Suggestion(s) for extension
Challenge the children to built up subtraction patterns using other numbers. Get them to record their results in a systematic way, as above. Ask the children to start a pattern and get a friend to finish it. Encourage the children to use the terms 'even', 'odd', 'increasing' and 'decreasing' in describing their patterns.

Suggestion(s) for support
Discuss the children's understanding of patterns and check their subtraction. If the need for support lies within pattern, work with the children on more simple subtraction patterns. If the need for support lies with subtraction, undertake addition patterns only for the time being.

Assessment opportunities
Are the children able to find several ways of making calculations that have the same answer? Observe individual children as they put their calculations into a systematic

Previous skills/knowledge needed
Children should understand the value of numbers to 20 and be able to add and subtract to 20.

Preparation
Prepare two number grids, one with numbers up to 25 and the other with numbers to 100, by filling in copies of the blank grids on photocopiable pages 124 and 125. Copy them so that there is one of each for each child.

1	2	3	4	5
6	7	8	9	10
11	12	13	14	15
16	17	18	19	20
21	22	23	24	25

1	2	3	4	5	6	7	8	9	10
11	12	13	14	15	16	17	18	19	20
21	22	23	24	25	26	27	28	29	30
31	32	33	34	35	36	37	38	39	40
41	42	43	44	45	46	47	48	49	50
51	52	53	54	55	56	57	58	59	60
61	62	63	64	65	66	67	68	69	70
71	72	73	74	75	76	77	78	79	80
81	82	83	84	85	86	87	88	89	90
91	92	93	94	95	96	97	98	99	100

Copy blank grid cards for each child using photocopiable pages 124 to 125. Make recording sheets for each child using photocopiable pages 126 and 127. For the support activity, make a set of multiplication calculation cards for each child.

Resources needed
Counters, number grids, blank grids (from photocopiable pages 124 and 125), pencils, recording sheet from photocopiable pages 126 and 127, calculator.

What to do

Distribute a copy of the 1–25 number grid to each child. Discuss the grid as a group. How many columns are there? How many rows? Can the children find any patterns in the grid by looking at it? Some children may recognise that all the numbers in the last row begin with 2; that the numbers go up in 1s; that the numbers in the last column end in 0 or 5 and this column might represent numbers they already know as a sequence: 5, 10, 15, 20, 25.

Invite the children to work individually and go along the grid in multiples of two, using counters to cover the numbers. Ask questions and make comments to help them describe the pattern they have made on the grid, for example: 'If you start on 2 what is the next number going to be? How do you know? What number are we adding on each time? We are counting in 2s.'

Now ask the children to study their completed grid. What do they notice about the numbers they have covered with counters? Can they describe the pattern? For example, 2, 8, 14 and 20 down one diagonal and 4, 8, 12 and 16 along another diagonal. Tell the children that these are all even numbers. Encourage the children to record their numbers on the recording sheet, beginning with 2.

Now ask the children to use the grid to count in 2s again, but this time starting on 1. Once again, use questioning to help the children to understand that these are all odd numbers.

Ask the children to count in 5s. Discuss the results again, and help the children to notice the patterns they create as the sequence is developed. Can they predict the next number

in the sequence on the basis of what they have done so far? They should record their results as they go along. Discuss the patterns that result, then ask the children how many numbers they have covered over. Does this tell them anything? Ask the children if, from this pattern, they can work out how many 5s are needed to make 25? What other sums can they make up using this pattern? For example: one lot of 5 is 5; two lots of 5s are 10.

Ask the children to complete the record sheet on page 126.

Distribute the blank grids from photocopiable page 124 and talk to the children about the different kinds of grid shown on it. Ask them to choose one and complete it by filling in their own numbers. They can then make up their own patterns by using multiples of 2, 3, 4 or 5 using the different grids. As before, help them to discuss their results.

Ask them to record a multiplication pattern they have created and ask a friend to describe the pattern.

		3		
6			9	
	12			15
		18		
21			24	

Now ask the children to work in pairs. Each member of the pair should start a pattern on the 1–25 number grid without saying what the multiple is. They should then cover the first three numbers with the counters. Ask them to look at each other's grids and continue that pattern, saying what the multiple is. Ask them to predict the next number in the pattern. Explain that they should each check the results and describe the patterns which have been formed. Then ask them each to make up two multiplication sums based on the pattern and compare them.

1 set of three **3** 2 sets of three **6** 3 sets of three **9**

Extend this idea to the use of a 1–100 number grid. Encourage counting using counters and recording multiples of 2, 5 and 10. Now ask the children to work in pairs, and explain that each child should start a pattern on the grid without saying what the multiple is. Tell them to cover the first three numbers with the counters and ask their partners to guess the pattern and finish it, saying what the multiple is. They can also write down what the next number in the pattern would be. Get each child to check their partner's results and describe the patterns which have been formed. Ask the children to describe their number patterns in the blank boxes on the recording sheet on page 127.

Finally, distribute blank copies of the blank 10 × 10 grid. Encourage the children to make up their own patterns using

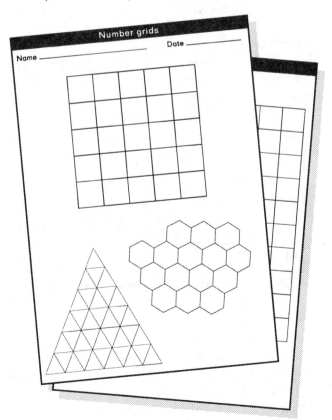

multiples of 2, 3, 4 or 5. They should discuss their results as above and make up multiplication calculations based on the pattern.

Suggestion(s) for extension
Ask the children to work with a friend and use a calculator and grid. One child should think of a number and ask her partner to make up the multiplication sum on the calculator.

Suggestion(s) for support
Some children will only be able to work on the 5 × 5 grid and complete their own grid. Ask them to make up a pattern of

their own and tell you about it. Ask them to look for a pattern of 2 by covering every other number. Which numbers have they covered? Can they tell you the next number to cover?

Assessment opportunities
Note whether the children are able to predict the next number in a pattern. Do they recognise the pattern which is being formed? Note whether they can apply the pattern to solve multiplication calculations. Check their recording cards for evidence of their ability to note the sequence of numbers in the pattern. With reference to this, ask them what multiple was being used to generate this sequence of numbers. Have they identified multiplication patterns of at least 2, 5 and 10?

Display ideas
Display some of the children's completed grids. Ask the

children to write descriptions of what they have found out beside each one.

Reference to photocopiable sheets
Photocopiable pages 124 and 125 offer blank number grids which can be completed as required and used for counting in multiples using counters. Photocopiable pages 126 and 127 provide children with a recording sheet for their patterns.

The grids used for this activity are multipurpose and can be used for a wide range of investigations. Once completed, the children's personal 100 square can be kept as a reference and children should be encouraged to use them when solving multiplication problems.

ADDITION AND SUBTRACTION BOARD GAMES

To be able to recall number facts using addition and subtraction to 12 quickly and accurately.
†† *Pairs.*
⏱ *30–40 minutes.*

Previous skills/knowledge needed
Children should understand the processes of addition and subtraction. They should, for instance, have had lots of experience in matching members of sets to establish addition and subtraction patterns.

Preparation
Use the blank number grid on photocopiable page 124 to make the two boards shown below. Make card copies of the number grids for each pair. These can be coloured in and then laminated or covered in clear plastic adhesive.

7	12	10	6	3
6	4	9	6	8
8	6	2	5	7
4	9	8	7	5
11	10	7	9	7

Addition board game

5	3	1	2	5
0	1	0	5	1
0	2	0	3	0
3	5	2	4	4
4	2	1	3	4

Subtraction board game

Resources needed
Two numbered dice (one of which should be marked 0 to 5) for each pair, two dotted dice marked 1 to 3 (for support activity), two number grid game boards made from photocopiable page 124, a set of same colour counters for each player, pencil and writing materials (optional).

What to do

Distribute counters, copies of the addition board game and two dice (one of which should be marked 0 to 5) to each pair of children. Explain that the children should then take it in turns to throw the dice and total the score. If this number is on the board they should cover it with a counter, each child using a counter of a different colour. When all the numbers have been covered, count up the counters of each colour. The person with the most counters on the board is the winner.

Let the children play the game several times and encourage them to keep account of who is the winner each time. You might ask the children to record their calculations on paper as a check.

When the children are confident with this game, distribute counters, copies of the subtraction board game and two dice, one of which should be marked 0 to 5, to each pair. Explain that the children should again take it in turns to throw the dice, but this time they should subtract the smaller number from the larger. If the resulting number is on the board they can cover it with a counter. As before, when all the numbers have been covered, count up the counters. The person with the most counters on the board is the winner.

Again, let the children play the game several times and ask them to keep account of who is the winner each time. You might ask the children to record their calculations on paper as a check.

Suggestion(s) for extension

Challenge the children to make up their own board games using three dice – including one marked 0 to 5. Discuss with them what numbers will need to be on the board. Help them to design the board and let them play some addition games. This could be further developed by letting them play using two dice, including one marked 0 to 5, with the players deciding whether to use addition or subtraction after each throw. Once again, whoever has the most counters on the board at the end of the game is the winner.

The children should then be encouraged to discuss which strategies they were using, i.e. when was it wise to choose a subtraction procedure rather than to use an addition procedure.

Suggestion(s) for support

Use two dice dotted 1 to 3 for the addition game and encourage the children to count the dots on both dice. If children become confident at this, replay the games in the main activity later, still using the dice marked with numbers 1 to 3.

Assessment opportunities

Note how accurately (and quickly) the children recall the number facts. Do some children need the aid of counters? Notice whether some of the children are counting on or counting back rather than using addition and subtraction.

Opportunities for IT

Children could be invited to make up their own board games and use a word processor to write and print out the instructions for someone else to play the game. A graphics package could be used to decorate it. Children should save their rules on to a disk so that they can retrieve them later for amending should they need to modify the rules as they play.

NUMBER OF THE DAY

To build up a knowledge of the relationship between number facts; to be able to identify several number facts related to a single answer.

†† *Whole class discussion, then individual work, then whole class for concluding discussion.*

🕐 *20–30 minutes.*

Previous skills/knowledge needed

The children should understand the processes of addition and subtraction. They should, for instance, have had lots of experience in matching members of sets to establish differences.

Preparation

Have ready a large sheet of card or sugar paper on which to record the number facts. Write on the heading 'Number of the day'.

Resources needed
Large sheet of card, paper, writing materials, counters (optional).

What to do
Tell the class that over the next few weeks on every day they will try to discover and record as many facts as they can for numbers between 1 and 20. Each morning, pick a 'number for the day', for example 15, (although when introducing the activity it would be best to start with a low number) and encourage the children to think of some addition sums they can make up to which the answer is 15. Explain that they should use just two numbers first, and then if they wish go on to use three and four numbers. Write out their suggestions on the board or flip chart. If some children are finding it difficult to think of sums, encourage them to use a systematic approach. For example, if one child says '10 and

5 is 15', write it (10 + 5 = 15) and then ask 'What must I add to 11 to make 15?', writing 11 + ? = 15 underneath. By doing this you will find that one column is increased by 1 while the other is reduced by 1.

Ask the children to work individually to make up as many calculations as they can to make 15. Discuss how many numbers they used for the addition calculations, for example:

    1 + 2 + 3 + 9 = 15 (4 numbers)

    5 + 5 + 5 = 15 (3 numbers)

    10 + 5 = 15 (2 numbers)

As children record their calculations, help them to apply their knowledge of the patterns of number. Encourage the children to go on to look at the subtraction facts they can make where 15 is the answer.

In a whole-class discussion, ask the children to state some of their number facts and record them for display on the chart. Discuss how the children devised all their calculations.

Talk about the strategies they used. For example, if a child began with 20 – 5 = 15, the next sum might be 19 – 6 = 15, then 18 – 7 = 15 and so on.

Show children how to adopt a systematic approach to working out all the number facts. Talk about the advantages of working this way, for example they would be less likely to miss any of the facts and it would help them remember the facts because they can see the pattern, i.e. it becomes predictable.

Suggestion(s) for extension
Encourage the children to make up multiplication and division calculations based on the number. They might like to use a calculator to explore some larger subtraction bonds, for example: 59 – 44 = 15; 115 – 100 = 15; 1216 – 1201 = 15.

Suggestion(s) for support
Work on addition facts only and work with these children to ensure they have strategies for building up the number. They could use a calculator to try out some numbers and then check using counters or cubes. Start by getting them to add only two numbers, then progress to three numbers if appropriate.

Assessment opportunities
Note the children's ability to manipulate numbers in their head. Can they recall number facts quickly? Do they adopt a systematic approach to building up the number or is it based on a random approach? Help pupils to adopt a systematic strategy. Identify children who need further opportunities to develop this skill.

Display ideas
Display the number of the day recording chart in a prominent place in the classroom.

NUMBER QUIZ

To know the number facts in the 2, 5 and 10 times tables.

†† *Pairs.*

⏲ *20–30 minutes.*

Previous skills/knowledge needed
Children should understand the value of numbers to 20 and be able to add and subtract to 20. They should know addition and subtraction facts to 20 at least.

Preparation
Make copies of the number calculation cards and answer cards from photocopiable pages 128 to 130 for each child by copying the pages on to card, laminating them and cutting out the individual sums.

Resources needed

Counters (optional), number calculation and answer cards, pencils, calculators, a number line.

What to do

Introduce the children to multiplication, perhaps by reminding them of the work they might have done in 'Number grids' (page 40). Distribute the multiplication cards based on 2. Ask the children to take turns to test each other on the calculations. (They do not need to record the results as the time should be spent on mental calculations.) If necessary let them use the counters to check the answers. Now distribute the answer cards and let the children match the sums with the answers.

Collect up all the sum cards and leave the answer cards in a pile on the table face up. Working in their pairs, each child should then take an answer card and decide which sum it belongs to. The children may wish to record their results on paper for you to check or they can use a calculator to check their own results.

Once they have worked through all the answer cards, the children can shuffle all the cards and play a version of snap, matching the sums to the right answers.

Collect the answer cards and put them to one side, and give a basic calculator to one member of each pair. Get the children to stack the sum cards face up on the table. Explain that they are going to play a game called 'Outsmart the calculator'. Tell them how one child must use the calculator to work out the answer to the sum on the card while the other must work it out in his head. Whoever calculates the

10 x 1	10 x 2	10 x 3	10 x 4
5 x 1	5 x 2	5 x 3	5 x 4
2 x 1	2 x 2	2 x 3	2 x 4
2 x 5	2 x 6	2 x 7	2 x 8
2 x 9	2 x 10	2	4
6	8	10	12
14	16	18	20

10s number
2s number quiz cards

answer first can take the card and the winner is the child with the most cards. Once they have played one game, allow the children to swap over so that they each have a turn using the calculator.

Once the children have worked through the activities using the cards based around 2, distribute the cards based on 5 and repeat the activities.

Finally, let them play the same game using the cards based on 10.

Suggestion(s) for extension

Encourage the children to make up their own sums to give specific answers using any operation they wish, including division.

Suggestion(s) for support

Do all the activities outlined above but concentrate only on the multiplication facts relating to 2. Ask the children to make a pattern using multiples of 2 on a 25-square or 5 × 5 grid (see photocopiable page 124). Use this to assist with establishing the multiplication facts. Refer to the class number line, and ask the children to, for example, count the jumps from the beginning to 8. Help the children to record these number facts by writing them on to their own sheets of card.

Assessment opportunities

By observing the children matching the cards, playing snap and devising calculations to match the 'answers', decide which individuals know the number facts in the 2, 5 and 10 times tables. Identify those who need further support and practice.

Distinguish between those who need further support in the more fundamental aspect of understanding the process of multiplication and those who need further exposure to the facts themselves through the sorts of games and activities described above.

Reference to photocopiable sheets

Photocopiable pages 128 to 130 provide sum and answer cards which can be used both for matching games and for playing snap. They can also be used in the following activity.

NUMBER CHAINS (1)

To recognise that subtraction is the inverse of addition; to be able to use subtraction as the inverse of addition.

†† *Individual work which could be undertaken by a large group at a time.*

🕐 *30–40 minutes.*

Previous skills/knowledge needed

Children should understand the processes of addition and subtraction. They should, for instance, have had lots of experience in matching members of sets to establish differences between numbers and or understanding of addition and subtraction patterns.

Preparation

Make several copies of photocopiable page 131 for each child. Seat the children at tables where they can work

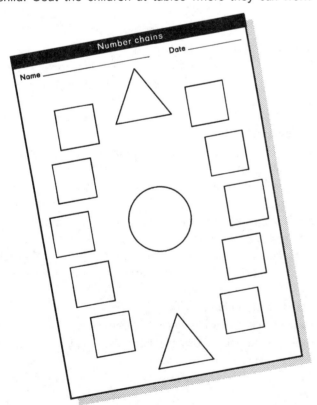

individually. Make sure they can see you and hear you giving the instructions for using the photocopiable page.

Resources needed

Copies of photocopiable page 131, paper, writing materials, counters (optional), calculators for support activity.

What to do

Remind the children about addition and subtraction patterns and ask the children to give you some examples. Distribute a copy of photocopiable page 131 to each child. Point out the squares and the two triangles. Explain to the children that they must think of a number between 1 and 5 and should write it in the triangle at the top of the page. They should then think of another number between 1 and 5 which they can use to add on. They should add this one to the first one and write the result in the square beside the triangle, for example △3 add on ☐2 gives ☐5 add on another ☐2 gives ☐7 etc.

They should keep adding that number and writing the total in successive squares until they reach the triangle. Ask the children to go back around the circle subtracting their number. Where do they finish? Why do they think this happens?

Discuss with the whole class what has happened and draw their attention to the pattern which is formed.

Encourage the children to try doing it again starting with a different triangle number and discuss the result as before.

Suggestion(s) for extension

Ask the children to make up their own number chains ensuring that they return to their original number each time.

Suggestion(s) for support

Encourage the children to use a calculator or counters to help them with the addition and subtraction. Some children may find it helpful to work in a small group with each child beginning with the same number. After they have worked in a small group on one example, encourage them to work on their own. Give them help as necessary.

Assessment opportunities

Note the children's ability to appreciate that subtraction is the inverse of addition. Do they know why they ended up with the same number? Ask them to explain to you and use their completed sheets as evidence.

Reference to photocopiable sheets

Photocopiable page 131 provides the children with a board which can be used to develop the notion of subtraction being the inverse of addition. It can also be used for the following activity.

NUMBER CHAINS (2)

To recognise that division is the inverse of multiplication; to be able to use division as the inverse of multiplication.

†† *Individual work which could be undertaken by a large group at a time.*

🕐 *30–40 minutes.*

Previous skills/knowledge needed

Children should understand the process of multiplication and division.

Preparation

Make several copies of photocopiable page 131 for each child.

Resources needed

Copies of photocopiable page 131, paper, writing materials, one calculator per child.

What to do

Remind the children about multiplication and division patterns and ask them to give you an example. Distribute one copy of photocopiable page 131 to each child and one basic calculator. Point out the squares and the two triangles. Explain to the children that they must think of a number between 1 and 5 and write it in the triangle on the top of the page. They should then think of another number between 1 and 5, multiply this one by the first one and write the result in the square beside the triangle. Tell them to keep multiplying by that number and writing the total in successive squares until they reach the triangle. Ask the children to go back around the circle dividing by their number instead. They can use a

calculator to help them. They should keep dividing by that number until they get back to the triangle.

As a whole class, discuss what happened. What number do they finish with? Why? Draw attention to the patterns which were formed and suggest that they try doing it again with a different number. Discuss the result as before.

Suggestion(s) for extension

Encourage the children to select numbers between 5 and 10, and then between 10 and 20. Ask them to make up their own multiplication and division chains.

Suggestion(s) for support

Some children may find it helpful to work in a small group with each child starting with the same number and then working together to get back to the same number. Let them use a calculator. Having worked in this way, now encourage the children to work on their own. Give them help as necessary.

Assessment opportunities

Note children's ability to appreciate that division is the inverse of multiplication. Why did they end up with the same number? Do they know why? Ask them to explain to you. Use their completed sheets as evidence.

Reference to photocopiable sheets

Photocopiable page 131 provides the children with a board which can be used to develop the notion of division being the inverse of multiplication.

DISCOVER MORE NUMBER FACTS

To be able to predict unknown number facts using a doubling technique.

†† *Pair work followed by whole class or large group work.*

🕐 *30–40 minutes.*

Previous skills/knowledge needed

Children should have an understanding of the process of addition and subtraction. They should know the number facts in the 2, 5 and 10 times tables.

Preparation

Prepare number calculation and answer cards as described in the 'Number Quiz' on page 44 for each pair. Prepare a large sheet of card divided into two columns headed 'Multiplication numbers we know' and 'Multiplication numbers we discovered'.

Resources needed

Large markers in two different colours, large sheet of card, paper, writing materials, counters or calculators (optional), sum and answer cards from photocopiable pages 129 to 130.

What to do

Distribute the multiplication sums and answers based on 5 (photocopiable page 129). Ask the children to match the sums with the answers, and sequence them in order on the table. Encourage the children to talk about this by asking questions: 'What do we know about counting in 5s? What do you notice about the last digit each time? We are counting on in 5s when we multiply successive numbers by 5.'

Now ask the children if they can discover a way of building up all the facts about 10 by using the facts they already know about 5 to help them. Allow children time to talk about this in pairs. Help them by asking such questions as: 'Is 10 bigger or smaller than 5? How much bigger is it? We know it's twice as big as 5, does that help us? Would 10 involve bigger or smaller jumps? What number are you counting in?' and so on. Help them to establish that since 10 is twice as big as 5, all the answers will also be twice as big

when they are multiplied by 10 instead of 5.

On the basis of all the facts they know about 5, let the children devise the same number of facts about 10. Ask the children to write down their discoveries in pairs. Next ask them to assist you to complete the 'Multiplication numbers we knew/Multiplication numbers we discovered' chart. Get the children to call out to you facts based on 5 and then to offer the corresponding fact based on 10, for example:

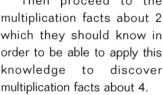

> Multiplication numbers we knew
>
> **1 x 5 = 5**
>
> Multiplication numbers we discovered
>
> **1 x 10 = 10.**

As the children call out the facts, fill out the chart in two colours, for example red pen for the 5s and a green pen for the 10s.

Finally, go through the same procedure to help children discover multiplication facts about 4 from known multiplication facts about 2.

Suggestion(s) for extension

Ask the children to consider how they would go about discovering the facts about 6, 7 and 15.

Suggestion(s) for support

Start by using the addition facts of 5 as an example. Help children to discover the addition facts about 4 from addition facts about 2. Make a chart as described above to help explain the process. Ask questions such as 'Why can we work out all the facts about 4 from the facts about 2?'

Then proceed to the multiplication facts about 2 which they should know in order to be able to apply this knowledge to discover multiplication facts about 4.

Assessment opportunities

Observe just one or two children during the discussion. Be aware of what strategies they are applying. Are they involved in the discussion? Do they contribute sensible suggestions? Did they grasp the notion of doubling in order to build up new facts? Are there some children who need more experience doing this type of activity? Make a note of those who seem to understand the idea fully. Did they succeed in discovering the facts for 7 and 15?

Number relationships

Display ideas

Display the 'Multiplication numbers we knew' and 'Multiplication numbers we discovered' charts in a prominent place in the classroom.

Reference to photocopiable sheets

Photocopiable pages 129 to 130 offer children the 'known' facts from which they can then establish the 'unknown' facts. (These are also used in the 'Number quiz' described above.)

ZERO

To recognise that zero represents an empty set and understand its use as place holder in the place value system.

✝✝ *Group of four to six children.*

🕒 *20–30 minutes.*

Previous skills/knowledge needed

Children should be able to complete tasks involving one-to-one correspondence and be able to use the language of ordinal numbers correctly.

Key background information

It is important to note that the notion of zero or nothing or the empty set is a difficult concept for the young child to grasp. While children may have little or no difficulty grasping the concept of a physical collection of objects, they may not understand the possibility of *nothing* (0) corresponding to *nothing*. Children need to see zero as a number rather than a symbol for the absence of a number. The pet corner in the classroom may, for example, contain 2 hamsters, 3 goldfish and 0 dogs.

Preparation

Collect together lots of counting materials for example beads, counters or interlocking cubes. Collect ten containers with lids: put counters or cubes in six tins and leave the other four empty. Replace the lids.

Resources needed

Ten containers with lids, counting materials (for example, counters, cubes), adhesive labels, pens, number line.

What to do

Place the containers in the middle of the table. Ask one child to select a container, shake it and listen carefully to the noise it makes, then guess how many counters are inside. Ask her to pass the container on to the next child and repeat the process. Continue in this way until all the children have had a turn. Ask questions such as, 'When you shake the container, what do you hear? How many counters are inside? How can you tell if there aren't any counters inside?' Let the children open the container and check. When the children find an empty container, remind them 'Zero is silent; zero counters make no noise' and encourage the children to say that there are no counters in the container or there is nothing in the container. The response to the question 'How many counters are in the container?' should be 'There are zero counters in the container.' Continue until all the containers have been opened and checked. Use the language associated with zero and ask questions to encourage the children to use this language.

Ask the children to look at your empty hand. Close it and tell the children that you have no sweets in your hand. Then ask them how may sweets you have in your hand. The answer should be zero.

Now tell the children you need to put more counters in each container, and add, say 2 to each. Ask what happens to the containers with zero counters? How many are in those containers now?

Next take out some counters, for example two, and invite children to predict how many will be left in each container after taking out that number.

Suggest that all the containers should now be labelled with the correct number of counters in each. Open each container and decide with the children how to label each one. Discuss the label for zero – what should be put on this label?

Finally, the children can stick labels on to the containers and write on the correct number.

Suggestion(s) for extension

Refer to zero on your number line. Ask the children to count on from zero; count in 2s from zero to 10. Make some more sets with different numbers of items in them, including a zero set.

Suggestion(s) for support

Encourage discussion about *'nothing'* and *'zero'* with reference to the things in the classroom, for example: 'This is an empty pencil case: it has zero pencils. This is an empty cup: it has nothing in it.' Help the children to make up their own statements using zero and nothing.

Assessment opportunities

On the basis of the discussion, decide which children grasped the idea of zero and nothing.

Display ideas

Make sets of items and include an empty set. Decorate the containers and make one set of digit cards to display beside the containers. Ask a group of children to put a different number of cubes in each container, making sure that there is at least one empty one. Leave the containers and digit cards on display for other groups of children to listen and guess, then place a card beside each container.

ODD AND EVEN

To be able to identify odd and even numbers.

†† *Pairs.*

🕐 *30 minutes.*

Previous skills/knowledge needed

Children should be able to complete tasks involving one-to-one correspondence and be able to use the language of ordinal number correctly. They should appreciate the value of numbers to 10 and know addition bonds to 12.

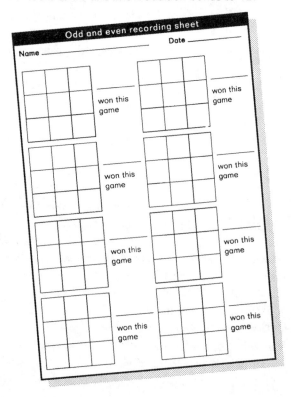

Preparation

A useful preparation for this activity is for children to find partners in a PE activity and emphasise whether or not everyone has a partner. Make copies of photocopiable page 132. For extension activity: make copies of photocopiable page 124 and cut out the 5 × 5 grid.

Resources needed

Two dice, Unifix cubes, a copy of photocopiable page 132 for each child. For extension activity: 5 × 5 grid from photocopiable page 124.

What to do

Tell the children that you want them all to find partners in order to play a game. Remind them of any other previous occasion where they needed a partner. Ask the children to form two lines and see if they can make pairs. If someone is left without a partner, explain to them that there is an odd number in the group/class or if everyone has a partner explain that there is an even number of children in the class.

Distribute 16 Unifix cubes to each pair and ask them to build two towers of equal height. Discuss whether they can build two equal towers using just one cube. Two cubes? Three cubes?

How many cubes did they use to build both towers? Are the towers the same height? Establish that the numbers of cubes used to build towers of equal heights are *even numbers*. Make sure that the children are given several opportunities to make towers of equal height and that they then count the total number of cubes it took to make these two towers. Stress that this number has to be an even number.

Now give each pair two dice and a copy of photocopiable page 132. Explain that they are going to play a game similar to noughts and crosses. Ask each child to decide whether to be 'Even' or 'Odd'. The first child, who is, say, 'Even' throws the two dice, and adds the two scores. She must then decide whether the number she gets is an even number or an odd number. If she decides it is an even number, she can write it anywhere on the first grid on the recording sheet. However, if it is an odd number she cannot write anything. Encourage the children to use the strategy of building equal towers to establish whether a given number is odd or even.

Eventually, the children should be able to dispense with this strategy, but encourage them to use it if there is any uncertainty.

The game continues with the player who is 'Odd' writing odd numbers on the grid. The aim of the game is to get three

2		
4	3	
6	9	7

'odd' or 'even' numbers in a line, whether a row, a column or a diagonal line. Whoever does this first is the winner.

Suggestion(s) for extension
Ask the children to explore numbers from 11 to 20, sorting them into two sets – odd and even. Use the 5 × 5 number grid on photocopiable page 124 to identify and colour all the odd numbers in one colour and all the even numbers in another colour. What do the children notice?

Suggestion(s) for support
Ask the children to collect as many objects from around the classroom as they can find to make pairs. They can then collect three objects which can be displayed as one pair and one odd one left over. They can then start using interlocking cubes to make pairs of even towers building up the pattern shown below:

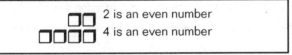

2 is an even number
4 is an even number

Assessment opportunities
Use the recording sheet as evidence of their understanding of odd and even numbers. Question individual children on how many games they won. Ask them to explain how they recognised odd and even numbers. Decide whether they can identify odd and even numbers to 10.

Reference to photocopiable sheets
Photocopiable page 132 can be used for recording the results of the game. Photocopiable page 124 shows the 5 × 5 grid which can be used for the extension activity.

SQUARE NUMBERS
To be able to recognise square numbers up to 100.
†† *Whole class, then individuals.*
🕐 *30–40 minutes.*

Previous skills/knowledge needed
To do this activity children need to be able to recognise a square and appreciate its properties.

Key background information
A square number can be represented by dots in the shape of a square for example:

Preparation
Make photocopies of pages 125 and 133 for each child. Children working on the extension activity will each need an extra copy of photocopiable page 125.

Resources needed
Collection of shapes (squares, rectangles and triangles), counters, copies of photocopiable pages 125 and 133. For extension activity: extra copies of photocopiable page 125.

What to do
Discuss the collection of shapes with the children and draw attention to their properties, for example: 'What can you say about all the sides of the square? Does it matter which way we turn the square? How is it different from a rectangle? from a triangle?'

Now ask the children to consider whether some numbers could be described as square: They can use the counters to help them. How would they check whether a number could be described as a square number? What would a square number have to show? Can they think of a way of discovering whether, for example, four is a square number? Listen to the children's responses and encourage them to reflect on their answers. Ask them each to take four counters and see if they can arrange them into a square. Help them to understand that there must be the same number of counters on each side and that all rows and columns should have the same number of counters.

Encourage the children to discuss whether it is possible to arrange the counters in a square. If so, they can conclude that 4 is a square number. Next ask them to explore the number 5 in this way. Help them to appreciate that they cannot arrange 5 counters in the same way as 4.

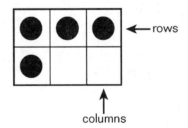

Explain that for the number to be square, the counters must be arranged so that the columns and rows have the same number of counters. Encourage them to use their blank 10 × 10 grid to record this and then try to make up other square numbers using the counters to help them. As they work, they should note down all the square numbers on the recording sheet and demonstrate how they know that number is square by illustrating the arrangement of the counters.

Suggestion(s) for extension
Help the children to realise by looking at the square patterns that a square number is the result of multiplying the two same numbers: 1 × 1; 2 × 2; 3 × 3; 4 × 4; 5 × 5; 6 × 6; 7 × 7;

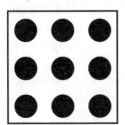

8 × 8; 9 × 9; 10 × 10; and so on. Make a multiplication square from the blank grid on page 125. Help children to identify the square numbers here and to see the pattern along the main diagonal.

Ask them to predict some more square numbers.

Suggestion(s) for support
Some children will find it helpful to work in a small group and only with numbers up to 25. Help the children to arrange the counters in various ways to discover whether they have made a square or not.

Assessment opportunities
Check the children's responses to your questioning. Note their approach to checking whether a number is square or not. Do they appreciate the notion of 'square'? The evidence

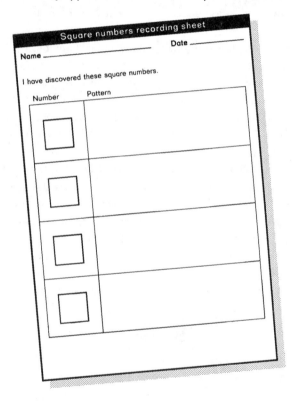

will come from your observation of what they do with the counters. Also use their recording sheets to assess whether they can now recognise square numbers to 100.

Display ideas
Make a book entitled *Our Square Numbers* by using coloured circular discs of paper. Display this in the classroom where children can refer to their own work and that of their peers as appropriate.

Reference to photocopiable sheets
Photocopiable page 133 can be used for recording the results. Photocopiable page 125 offers a blank 100-square which can be made into a multiplication square for the extension activity. The recording sheet should be completed as follows:

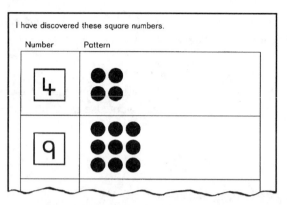

RECTANGULAR NUMBERS
To be able to establish several methods of arranging rectangular numbers such as 6, 12 and 24 in arrays.
†† *Whole class, then individuals.*
🕐 *30–40 minutes.*

Previous skills/knowledge needed
To do this activity, children need to be able to recognise a rectangle and appreciate its properties. It would be helpful if the children had previously undertaken the 'Square numbers' activity on page 51.

Key background information
A rectangular number can be represented by dots in the shape of a rectangle, for example:

Square numbers are included in the set of rectangular numbers for example:

Preparation
Prepare a copy of photocopiable pages 125 and 134 for each child. For the extension activity, prepare an extra copy of the blank 10 × 10 grid on photocopiable page 125 for each child.

Resources needed
A collection of shapes (squares, rectangles and triangles), counters, photocopiable pages 125 and 134.

What to do
Discuss the collection of shapes with the children. Ask questions which draw attention to their properties, for example, 'What can you say about all the sides of the rectangle? Does it matter which way we turn the rectangle? How is it different from a triangle?' and so on. Use some counters to make a rectangle, for example:

Now ask the children to consider whether some other numbers could be described as rectangular: 'How would you check whether a number could be described as a rectangular number? What would a rectangular number have to show?'

Ask them to take six counters each and see if they can arrange them into a rectangle. Explain that the two opposite sides must be equal, which means that there must be the same number of counters on opposite sides, the rows must have the same number of counters and the columns must have the same number of counters. However, the columns and rows need not have the same number of counters. Encourage the children to discuss whether it is possible to arrange the counters in a rectangle, and lead them to conclude that 6 is a rectangular number.

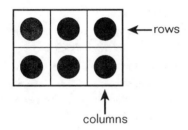

Next ask them to explore the number 5 in this way. Help them to appreciate that the following is not indicative of a rectangular number:

To be rectangular, the counters must be arranged so that the two columns contain the same number of counters and the two rows have the same number of counters. Let them use the 10 × 10 grid from photocopiable page 125 to make some more rectangular numbers using counters to help them.

Distribute photocopiable page 134 (for recording purposes) to each child, and explain that you want them to go on from 6 to 20 and see if they can find other rectangular numbers. Tell them that they should use the counters to discover whether a number is rectangular or not. As they work, encourage them to note down all the rectangular numbers on the recording sheet and show how that number is rectangular by illustrating the arrangement of the counters.

Suggestion(s) for extension
Make a multiplication square from the 10 × 10 grid. Help the children to identify the rectangular numbers here and to see if there is a pattern. From a given sequence of rectangular numbers, is it possible to say what the next number will be?

Suggestion(s) for support
Work with a small group to do the tasks described above, going as far as 20. Help the children to arrange the counters in various ways to discover whether or not they have made a rectangle.

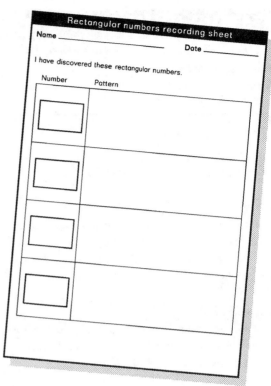

Assessment opportunities
Check children's responses to your questioning. Note their approach to checking whether a number is rectangular or not. Firstly, do they appreciate the notion of 'rectangle'? The evidence will come from your observation of what they do with the counters. Also use their recording sheets to assess whether they can now recognise rectangular number to 20.

Display ideas
Make a book entitled 'Our rectangular numbers' using coloured circular discs to create the rectangle numbers. Display this in the classroom where children can refer to their own work and that of their peers as appropriate.

Reference to photocopiable sheets
Photocopiable page 134 can be used for recording the results. For the extension activity, photocopiable page 125 can be used to make a multiplication square. The recording sheet should be completed in a way similar to that shown below.

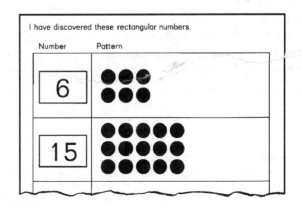

NEGATIVE NUMBERS

To begin to recognise numbers and to know that they represent amounts below zero.

†† *Pairs.*

🕐 *20–30 minutes.*

Previous skills/knowledge needed
They need to appreciate the process of subtraction and realise that subtraction is the inverse of addition.

Preparation
Check that all the calculators to be used record minus numbers in the same way, usually the number followed by the minus sign (e.g. 2–). Make a copy of the recording sheet on photocopiable page 135 for each child.

Resources needed
Copies of the recording sheet on page 135, a calculator for each pair of children, photocopiable page 111 (blank dot-to-dot picture) for extension activity.

What to do
Talk to the children about using a calculator for subtraction sums. Ask them to call out some subtraction sums for their partners to do on the calculator.

Discuss how they should key in the numbers on the calculator. Ask the children to call out two numbers and decide which number to key in first. Ask them to reflect on what would happen if you tried to subtract, say, 9 from 7. Get them to key in ⑦, then ⊖, then ⑨, then ⊜.

What happens? Discuss the negative sign on the calculator display. 'What has happened? What does the sign mean? What is 2–? Is the 2– less than 2?' Tell the children that we call this the minus sign.

Ask them what is minus. Ask the children to draw a number line (see below) and decide where they would put zero, then 1, 2, 3, 4 and 5 on the strips you have prepared.

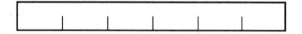

Next ask them if they could put –2 on the number line. Encourage the notion of extending the number line to the left and going from zero to –1 to –2 to –3 and so on to –5.

Ask them to think of other number combinations which might result in a negative number when they subtract. Ask them to explore these using the calculator. Extend the discussion with reference to the number line. Introduce the recording sheets. Ask the children to try out larger numbers for example, 3 subtract 24.

Suggestion(s) for extension
Encourage these children to use the calculator to complete the blank dot-to-dot picture (photocopiable page 111),

starting with zero and setting up a subtraction constant on the calculator. You may need to remind the children how to set up a constant function, for example:

Suggestion(s) for support
Work with a small group. Provide opportunities for individual responses based on their results. Help them to appreciate that –1 is less than 1 and less than 0 and so on. Use the number line as an aid.

The activity is different from the main activity only insofar as they should be given further opportunities to talk about and share their results.

Assessment opportunities
Check children's responses to your questioning. Do they appreciate the difference between 7 – 9 and 9 – 7? Are they able to express the fact that –2 is different from 2? Can they position zero on a number line and then see that –2 would come before 0 or 1 or 2? Do they use the term 'minus' or refer to negative numbers?

Reference to photocopiable sheets
Photocopiable page 135 can be used for recording the results in the main activity. The children will need to try out the completed example and then the incomplete example before trying out some of their own examples.

The extension activity requires the use of the blank dot-to-dot sheet on page 111 and each child can make up a different subtraction pattern starting from zero.

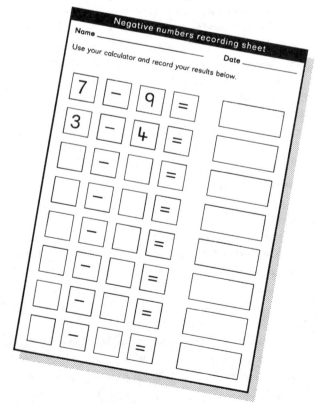

Calculations and problem solving

This section comprises operations, problems and checking activities. The activities on pages 56 to 63 cover operations, those on pages 64 to 69 cover problems and those on pages 70 to 76 address checking. The major aim underlying this chapter is an understanding of and the application of the processes involved.

Understanding the associated symbolisation of the operations is not a prerequisite to understanding, rather it follows understanding. Children who deal exclusively with symbols can be misled into thinking that the symbols exist in and of themselves rather than as representations of something else. The activities in this chapter deal with the children's own experiences and with real things while also helping to connect knowledge and understanding with the terminology and symbols that represent these concepts.

Operations constitute a key element of mathematics and children everywhere spend a great deal of 'maths time' carrying out simple operations. Conceptual understanding is most effectively developed through problem solving in a variety of contexts. Through having to apply operations and formulate solutions to problems, children develop both their reasoning abilities and their understanding of the operations. The activities in this chapter offer children the chance to find their own solutions, check their results, and work collaboratively as well as independently.

All the activities are designed to promote discussion, and offer the opportunity to assess thinking and conceptual understanding of the processes involved. Most include recording sheets which also provide access to understanding.

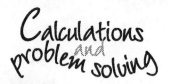
THE TOY SHOP

To recognise when addition and subtraction should be used; to be able to add and subtract within 10 quickly and accurately; to be able to use a variety of mathematical words and phrases to describe addition and subtraction.

†† *Groups of four to six children.*

🕐 *30–40 minutes.*

Previous skills/knowledge needed

Children should be able to count accurately to 10.

Key background information

Learning when to add and when to subtract is a lengthy process and takes a child far longer than we realise. For this reason it is necessary to spend considerable time exploring a variety of experiences which involve practical situations and concrete materials. The children should be encouraged to invent their own examples of addition and subtraction problems using apparatus. The aim is for the child to come to understand the process and purpose of addition and subtraction so well that they can identify in which circumstances to use them. This understanding is supported if children recognise the specialised language associated with addition and subtraction: *altogether, total, added, took away, less, more*, etc.

Preparation

Make laminated card copies of photocopiable page 136 for each child. Prepare ten sets of photocopiable page 137 for each group and cut them up.

Resources needed

For each child: toy shop cut from photocopiable page 136. For each group: ten sets of toy cards cut from photocopiable sheet 137. For the extension activity: paper and writing materials.

What to do

Give each child a copy of the toy shop and place toy cards in the middle of the table. Talk with the children about toy shops. What sorts of toys can they buy from a toy shop? Ask the children to identify the toys in the pictures.

Explain to the children that they are going to make up a story about their toy shops and the toys in the shop, for example: 'On Saturday there were 2 teddy bears in the shop. The shopkeeper went to the market and bought 4 more to put in her shop. Now there are 6 teddies in the shop.'

As you tell the story, pick up the appropriate number of toy cards and place them in the shop. Having told the story, ask the children if they can remember how many teddies the shopkeeper bought when she went to the market. How many did she have altogether?

Now 'clear the shop' and make up another story, for example: 'There were 4 trains in the shop. The shopkeeper went to the market and bought 4 more for the shop. How many trains were there altogether in the shop now?'

Having provided a few such examples of stories, help each child in the group to use the cards and make up their own stories that involve adding on to the existing number.

Help them to become familiar with the language associated with addition and subtraction by using it in your questions, for example: 'How many dolls are in the shop *altogether*? What is the *total* number of dolls in the shop? How many more teddies were *added* to the shop when the shopkeeper came back from the market?'

Encourage the children to use the same language in their questioning. As the children work, make sure that they recognise that they have been *adding*.

Now ask the children to take it in turns to make up stories that involve selling some of the toys, for example: 'The shopkeeper had 10 toy cars in the shop. 6 were sold. How many cars were left in the toy shop?'

Again the children should use the toy cards as props. Encourage them to listen to each other

The toy shop window

Toy cards

and to ask questions as they work: 'How many cars were sold? Are there less cars left in the shop now? How many less? How can you show what has happened?'

Ensure that the children realise that they have to take away 6 cars to show that 6 were sold and recognise that, in this example, they are *taking away* or *subtracting*.

Extend the stories so that they include 3 numbers to add or 2 numbers to add and 1 to subtract, or 2 numbers to subtract from an amount.

As they tell the stories, the children should pick out the required number of toy cards and record aloud as follows: '2 and 3 and 2 make 7 *altogether.*'

Help them to vary the language as follows: '2 and 3 add 2 gives me a *total* of 7.'

Let the children work in pairs and ask them to take it in turns to make up stories for each other. Each time the other child should ask a question.

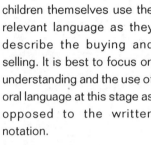

Discuss with the children what happens to the first number if another number is added or subtracted. Help them to recognise that addition increases the total and subtraction reduces it.

Suggestion(s) for extension

Ask the children to work in pairs, pooling their toys but using only one shop. By doing this they will be given the opportunity to add and subtract within 20, instead of 10.

Encourage the children to consider ways of recording what they have done and discuss with them the use of the plus and minus signs.

Suggestion(s) for support

Work with about six children in a large space in the classroom, before introducing them to aspects of the main activity. Make up some scenarios involving the children and help them to act out the mathematical language, for example:

▲ There are six birds in the nest (list the names of the six children in the group). Lynda, Amanda and Jason flew off to get food (they mime flying away). How many are still in the nest?

▲ Celene, Zoe and John are going to Robert's birthday party. When they arrive they play football with Robert and Sarah. How many children are at the birthday party altogether?

▲ There are five fish swimming in the lake (list names). Four

of the fish are caught. How many fish are still swimming in the lake?

Once the children have worked through a number of scenarios let them work on the original activity, as described above, but restrict the adding to smaller numbers.

Emphasise the use of mathematical language throughout and ensure the children themselves use the relevant language as they describe the buying and selling. It is best to focus on understanding and the use of oral language at this stage as opposed to the written notation.

Assessment opportunities

Observe individual children as they describe their shops. Do they use a range of mathematical words and phrases to explain what is happening? Do they do this confidently? Can they add and subtract quickly? After the discussion, note any children who know which operation (addition or subtraction) to use in a variety of situations.

Reference to photocopiable sheets

Photocopiable pages 136 and 137 offer children a shop and a set of toys which can be used in various ways.

CHANGE FROM 20 PENCE

To be able to subtract confidently and accurately within 20.

†† *Groups of four to six children.*

🕐 *30–40 minutes.*

Previous skills/knowledge needed

Children should be able to add within 20.

Key background information

This activity offers children the opportunity of giving change and finding the difference between two amounts by counting on.

For example, to work out what change must be given if 20 pence is offered for a 17 pence item, the children could start at 17 pence, and count forward to 20, giving a difference

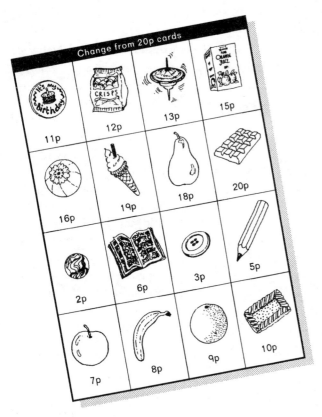

Change from 20p cards

change and as they do so you should encourage the use of mathematical language. For example: 'I will buy a bar of chocolate. This costs 20p so I will not be getting any change.' 'The ball costs 16p. I have 20p. I will get 4p change.'

The shopkeeper can give the required amount of change using any of the coins available, but encourage the children to apply their own strategies at this early stage.

Now encourage them to use a 'quick way' of deciding what change they need to have by counting on to 20 from the cost of the chosen item, for example: 'The crisps cost 12 pence. I need change from 20 pence. So I can count on to 20 from 12p. I must give 8p change.' Demonstrate this strategy by starting with items which cost, say, between 15 and 19 pence and then moving on to items which cost less. Ask question as follows: 'What change will I get if I buy an ice cream? What change will I get if I buy a packet of crisps?' and so on.

Continue by asking the children to buy two items from the shop with 20 pence. Here they might find the total cost of two articles before calculating the change they should get from 20 pence, or they may continue to use the counting on technique.

Suggestion(s) for extension
Ask the children to investigate all the combinations of two, then three, items they could buy for 20 pence or less, stating the amount of change involved in each case.

of 3. This procedure can also be used to establish the difference in value between two amounts of money. For example, Joanna has 15 pence and Elaine has 11 pence; how much more has Joanna than Elaine?

Preparation
Make laminated card copies of photocopiable pages 138 so that each group can have a set. Cut up the cards. Make another copy for each individual child, but do not cut it up. For the support activity, cut this sheet in half and use the lower half only.

Resources needed
For each group: a set of picture cards cut from photocopiable page 138, toy money up to the value of 20p, some 20p coins. For the support activity: some 10p coins, the lower part of photocopiable page 138.

What to do
Spread the set of cards on the table so that they are face up and discuss with the children what each item is. Help them to identify their prices. Can they pick out the most expensive and the least expensive items? Explain to the children that you are going to give each of them a 20p piece to spend and that they can choose just one of the items on display to buy. One child in the group should act as the 'shopkeeper'. Allow them plenty of time to select their items. Once they have chosen, they should buy it from the shopkeeper. They should work together with the shopkeeper to calculate the correct

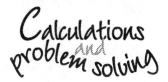

Suggestion(s) for support

Only use the cards with items up to 10 pence. Children can do all the above tasks but the change should be given out of 10 pence. They should select the correct amount of change and place it on the relevant picture on the lower half of the sheet. Check what each child has done and encourage them to say how they calculated the amount.

Assessment opportunities

Observe the strategies children are using to calculate the amount of change required. Have they grasped the notion of counting on? How confidently do they handle this? Check their pages with the appropriate amount of change: is this correct? This gives you evidence of how accurately they can subtract within 20.

Reference to photocopiable sheets

Photocopiable page 138 offers children a set of picture cards which can be used as a basis for giving change from 20 or 10 pence.

CHANGE FROM £1

To be able to subtract within 100 using apparatus.

†† *Small groups of three or four, then individual children.*

🕐 *30–40 minutes.*

Previous skills/knowledge needed

Children should know the addition and subtraction number bonds within 100. They should know that there are 100 pence in one pound. They should be able to count in 2s, 5s and 10s to 100.

Preparation

Make laminated card copies of photocopiable page 139 for each group and cut out the cards. Make another copy for each child, but do not cut it up.

Resources needed

For each group: a set of picture cards cut from photocopiable page 139, Dienes' apparatus or other counting apparatus, lots of toy coins to give change from one pound, including 10p, 5p, 2p and 1p coins, paper and writing materials (optional). For each individual: photocopiable page 139 (not cut out into cards). For support activity: the lower part of photocopiable page 139.

What to do

Spread the cards on the table face up. Help the children to identify the items and their prices. Explain that they can each have one pound to spend and that they can choose one item. Discuss the fact that a one pound coin is the same value as 100 pennies. Decide which child is going to be the

'shopkeeper' first. Give each child a pound coin. Allow them time to select their items and explore ways of giving the correct change. Encourage the use of mathematical language as follows: 'I will buy a pair of sunglasses. They cost 70 pence so I will get change from one pound.' Discuss ways of doing this. Ask for suggestions and discuss the responses.

Allow them to apply their own strategies and talk about what they did. Encourage them to use the coins in different ways. Did everybody use the same method?

Discuss, for example, counting on in 1s first and then in 10s: count in 1s to 20 pence (placing 1p coins on the table) and then continue in 10s: 30, 40, 50, 60, 70, 80, 90, one pound (placing a ten pence coin on the table each time).

Encourage the children to explore different ways and to explain their strategies to each other. 'The football costs 51 pence. I have one pound. I know there are two 50 pence

coins in one pound (taking two 50 pence coins) and I must pay 51 pence. There is 50 pence and take away one penny from that 50 pence which leaves 49 pence. The change I must get is 49 pence.'

Ask questions as follows: 'What change will I get if I buy the boat for 25 pence? What change will I get if I buy a kite for 12 pence?' and so on. Encourage them to use the coins as necessary.

Continue by asking children to buy two items from the shop with one pound. Here they might find the total cost of two articles before calculating the change they should get from one pound, or they may continue to prefer the counting on method.

Finally, distribute the photocopiable page 139 to each individual in the group. Ask them to decide what change out of one pound has to be given for each item. Tell them that they should select the correct amount of change from one pound, and place it on the relevant picture on the sheet.

Suggestion(s) for extension
Encourage children to investigate all the combinations of two, then three, then four items, they could buy for one pound, stating the amount of change involved in each case.

Suggestion(s) for support
Only use the cards costing more than 50 pence. Children can do all the above tasks but the change will be restricted to less than 50. Work with this group and encourage them to discuss the strategies they are using.

Assessment opportunities
Observe the strategies children are using to calculate the amount of change required. Have they grasped the notion of counting on? How confidently do they handle this? Check what each child has done and discuss with them how they calculated the amount of change to be given. Check their completed pages: did they give the correct amount of change?

Reference to photocopiable sheets
Photocopiable page 139 offers children a set of picture cards which can be used as a basis for giving change from one pound.

BEGINNING MULTIPLICATION

To recognise that multiplication is equivalent to repeated addition; to be able to complete simple multiplication calculations through repeated addition.

†† *Large group or whole class, then pairs.*

⏰ *30–40 minutes.*

Previous skills/knowledge needed
Children should be able to add together small numbers.

Key background information
The aim of this activity is to introduce children to the idea of multiplication being repeated addition. There should be no formal teaching of multiplication facts and no use of the 'x' sign at this stage.

Recognising, for example, two objects as *one* two is difficult and children need much experience of grouping and counting the groups in order to appreciate that *one* may refer to a group of two, three, four, five etc. Children therefore have to attend to two aspects:
▲ the number in the group;
▲ the number of groups.

Preparation
Arrange to work with a large group or the whole class first, then for pupils to work in pairs.

Resources needed
A collection of toy cars, a collection of coins including plenty of 2p, 5p, 10p and 20p coins, paper and writing materials, squared paper (for support activity).

What to do
Begin by asking two children to stand in front of the group.

Ask the class to note how many pairs of eyes the two children have between them. Record this on the board as follows:

$$2 + 2 = 4 \qquad 2 \text{ sets of } 2 = 4$$

Now ask another child to join them and make a similar recording as follows:

$$2 + 2 + 2 = 6 \qquad 3 \text{ sets of } 2 = 6$$

Continue in this way until you have about five or six sets of two recording each step on the board.

Now start again with different children, this time counting groupings of fingers of hands. Begin with two children and build up to five or six, recording as follows:

$$5 + 5 = 10 \qquad 2 \text{ sets of } 5 = 10$$
$$5 + 5 + 5 = 15 \qquad 3 \text{ sets of } 5 = 15$$

Then go on to groupings of ten by counting the number of fingers per person, again beginning with two people, and then adding one person and recording each additional *ten* as follows:

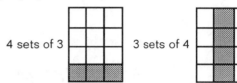

10 + 10 = 20   2 sets of 10 = 20

Continue until there are five or six sets of ten recorded in this way.

Next show children two toy cars, asking questions such as: 'How many wheels are there on each car? How many sets of wheels are there altogether?

Record the information as follows:

        4 + 4 = 8   2 sets of 4 = 8

Continue adding cars and recording the number of wheels, recording as follows:

4 + 4 + 4 + 4 + 4 + 4 + 4 = 28   7 sets of 4 = 24

Next get the children to work in pairs. Distribute a set of 2 pence, 5 pence, 10 pence and 20 pence coins to each pair. As before, encourage them to record how much money they have in two ways, for example:

10p + 10p + 10p + 10p + 10p = 50p   5 10p coins = 50p

Finally, ask the children to explain their recordings to other pairs and to the whole class. Encourage whole-class or large group discussion of the various groupings they made. Invite the children to think of other equal groupings from around the school, for example, the panes of glass in a window and the number of windows in the classroom, or the number of legs on a chair and the number of chairs in the classroom.

Suggestion(s) for extension

Ask the children to work from the opposite direction.

For example, write the following groupings on the board: 3 sets of 4; 3 sets of 5; 4 sets of 2; 6 sets of 3, and ask the children to think of different ways of displaying them, e.g. 3 sets of 4 or 4 + 4 + 4.

Suggestion(s) for support

Provide extra practice by using squared paper to demonstrate groupings, for example:

4 sets of 3   3 sets of 4

Ask the children to make up their own sets and addition sums using squared paper.

Assessment opportunities

Note the children's responses to your questioning. Can they reply confidently and accurately? Do they understand the recording process? Note which children, if any, need further practice in oral and practical work before doing their own recording.

BEGINNING DIVISION

To recognise that division is equivalent to repeated subtraction; to be able to complete simple division calculations through repeated subtraction.

†† *Whole class or large group, followed up by work in pairs.*

🕐 *30–40 minutes.*

Previous skills/knowledge needed

Children should be able to add and subtract within 20, and should know addition and subtraction facts to 20. They should also have a basic understanding of multiplication and should be able to recognise that multiplication is equivalent to repeated addition.

Key background information

The early stages of learning division involve the concepts of division as repeated subtraction and division as sharing. The first of these is the basis of this activity.

The idea of division as repeated subtraction can be illustrated by showing the children a purse of penny coins and asking the question: How many children can have three pence from this purse? Remove three pennies and give them to the first child, then another three to a second child and so on, until all the pennies have been distributed until there is not enough left to give out another three. Finally ask the children to count how many children have three pennies.

Preparation

Collect together different numbered sets of counting materials, e.g. a jar of 10 buttons, a jar of 20 buttons and a jar of 15 buttons; a box of 18 beads, a box of 24 beads and a box of 32 beads.

Resources needed

Collections of objects in containers as indicated above, 20 1p coins, a number line (for support activity), calculators (for support and extension activity), paper and writing materials.

What to do

Introduce the activity by displaying some of the containers. Select one of them and ask the children to estimate how many objects are in it. Then get the children to check how many objects there are. Ask the children how many times a set of 2 could be taken away from the container.

Record on the board how many objects are in the container and continue removing two until there are none left. Record each step by subtracting two as follows:

$10 - 2 - 2 - 2 - 2 - 2$

Count how many times two objects were taken out of the container. Encourage the children to say, for example, 'We took away 2 buttons five times. There are five 2s in 10.'

Proceed similarly with the remaining containers, recording the repeated subtraction and how many 2s or 3s and so on are in the total number.

(Note that no formal division or use of the division sign is attempted at this stage. Neither is there any teaching of the division facts.)

Next place 20 pennies in a pile on the table. Ask the children to estimate how many times you could take away a set of 4 pennies. Ask them to watch while sets of 4 pennies are taken away from the pile.

Ask them to help you to remember the number of times you took away 4 by recording it as follows:

$20 - 4 - 4 - 4 - 4 - 4$

Reinforce this by saying that this is 20, take away 4, take away 4, take away 4, take away 4 and take away another 4. Establish that you can take away 4 pennies from 20 pennies five times.

Make sure that all the children in the group get the opportunity to answer or ask questions and use this mathematical language.

Finally, ask the children to work in pairs and make up their own story using 12 pennies and taking away sets of 2 each time. Share their responses with the whole group by recording the results on the board.

The discussion should include the following questions: 'How many pennies did you start off with? How many pennies are there in each set? How many sets of 2 have you made? How many times can you take away a set of 2 pennies from 12 pennies?'

Encourage the children to record this as follows: 'With 12 you can make six sets of 2.'

Suggestion(s) for extension

Pose more challenging problems for these children to solve, for example, 'A group of five children share 26 sweets...' and so on. Discuss the ideas for the remainders.

Suggestion(s) for support

Children who need extra support could work through the first part of the main activity, down as far as the pair work. At this point, work with this group to give them further experience of division as repeated subtraction using the number line as an additional aid.

Encourage them to count back in 2s, 3s and so on, using

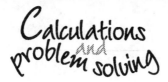
the number line. Alternatively or in addition, the idea of division as repeated subtraction could be reinforced using a calculator with a constant facility as follows:

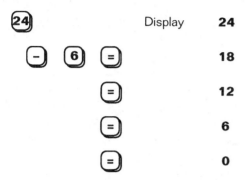

	Display	
[24]	**24**	
[–] [6] [=]	**18**	
[=]	**12**	
[=]	**6**	
[=]	**0**	

Encourage the children to describe this as follows:
24 – 6 – 6 – 6 – 6 = 0, and say, 'so I can take away 6 from 24 four times.'

Seek to achieve the learning objective with this group through further oral work and practical activity.

Assessment opportunities
Discuss the children's work with them, and note their responses to your questioning. Can they reply confidently and accurately? Note which children, if any, need further practice in oral and practical work before doing their own recording.

A BOARD GAME

To be able to use each of the four operations in simple situations; to be able to combine two operations in a calculation.
†† *Groups of three to four children.*
🕑 *30–40 minutes.*

Previous skills/knowledge needed
Children should have a basic understanding of the four operations.

Preparation
Copy photocopiable page 140 directly on to card or mount copies on to card. If possible, laminate the game board or cover it with clear adhesive plastic.

Copy photocopiable pages 141 to 144 directly on to card or mount them on to card. If possible, laminate or cover the cards with clear adhesive plastic, then cut out a set for each group.

Resources needed
For each pair or group: a set of question or sum cards cut from photocopiable sheets 141 to 144, a game board cut from photocopiable page 140, counters or board pieces, a dice, calculator (for extension activity).

What to do
Set up the game by placing all the sum cards on the table face down. Explain to the children how to play the game as follows.

The first player throws the dice and moves the board piece along the corresponding number of squares. If a player lands on a smiley face, she takes a sum card and answers the question. If her answer is correct (and all the players should check the answer), she gets another chance to throw the dice and move forward on the board. She also keeps the sum card. If she is wrong she must go back to the square she was on before she threw the dice. The winner is the first person to reach 'HOME'.

Suggestion(s) for extension
Ask the children to make up their own sum cards using a calculator to help them, and let them play the game again.

Suggestion(s) for support
Play the game as above, but only use the sum cards on photocopiable pages 141 and 142 which are based on addition and subtraction. Allow the children to use apparatus if necessary.

Assessment opportunities
Observe children as they solve the problems. Check their competence in dealing with the four operations. Identify any children who have difficulty with different aspects.

Is there a pattern to any difficulties, for example, getting the 'word' sums wrong, or those based on multiplication or division?

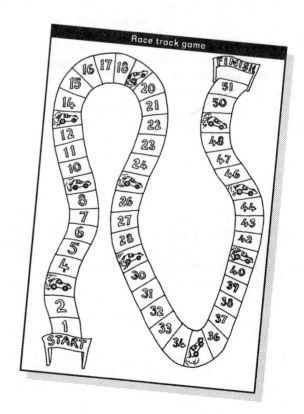

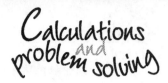
Reference to photocopiable sheets
Photocopiable pages 141 to 144 offer children a set sum cards to be used with photocopiable page 140, which is the game board.

THE CLASS SHOP

To be able to combine prices up to one pound; to be able to handle coins effectively.

†† *Four to six children initially, then pairs.*

🕐 *30–40 minutes.*

Previous skills/knowledge needed
Children should be able to do tasks involving one-to-one correspondence and they should understand ordinality. They should be able to recognise the various coins from one penny to one pound.

Preparation
Prepare a class shop containing a wide range of objects all priced up to one pound. You might like to link the theme of the shop to other work you might be undertaking at the moment, e.g. supermarket, café, bookshop, hardware shop, garden shop, pet shop etc. Make laminated card copies of photocopiable page 145. Cut out the labels and use them to label each item in the shop.

Resources needed
For each group: class shop containing a wide variety of items all labelled and price under one pound, toy money for use in shop ranging from one penny to one pound, and including 1p, 2p, 5p, 10p, 20p, 50p and £1 coins. For the extension activity: paper and writing materials.

What to do
Start the lesson by discussing the various items in the class shop and their prices. Get the children to identify each item and note its price. Decide together which are the most expensive and cheapest items in the shop. Ask lots of questions, for example: 'Which article costs the most money? Which costs the least money? Which items cost exactly one pound? Are there any things that cost exactly 50 pence? Can you find two things which cost less than 50 pence? How many things can you find which cost more than 75 pence?'

Give the children opportunities to ask each other questions. Allow them to take turns being the shopkeeper

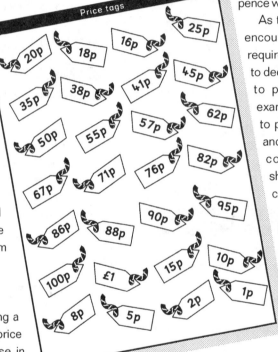
Price tags

answering the customers' questions about prices, for example: 'What are the two most expensive articles in the shop? What are the two cheapest things you can buy in this shop? Can you find six things for under one pound? Are there two items which cost less than 5 pence?'

Ensure the children are familiar with all the objects and their prices and that they can read the labels.

Give each child a collection of coins and proceed to tasks which involve addition as follows: 'Can you buy two things for under 10 pence? 20 pence? 50 pence? Are there three things for under 10 pence? 20 pence? 50 pence? Are there four things for under 10 pence? 20 pence? 50 pence? Can you buy three things for under one pound? How do you know you can buy all three for less than one pound? How can you make sure they will not cost more than one pound? Can you buy two things for over 50 pence with one pound? How do you know?'

As the children consider these tasks, encourage them to handle the money required for buying the items. Help them to decide which coins they need in order to pay the various amounts. For example: 'Which coins would you use to pay for xxx which costs 55 pence and yyy which costs 5 pence? Which coin(s) would you give to the shopkeeper to pay for the xxx which costs 35 pence?'

Suggestion(s) for extension
Ask the children to work individually to investigate the different ways they could spend less than one pound in the shop while buying only two items. They should also investigate the different ways they could spend more than one pound in the shop while buying only two items.

Suggestion(s) for support
Work with this group and go through similar questioning to that detailed above, but confine the addition work to two items.

Assessment opportunities
You may prefer to focus on just one or two children for assessment purposes. Evaluate their understanding on the basis of their responses to your questions and on the basis of their reactions to the tasks. Note whether they can combine prices to 10 pence, 20 pence, 50 pence and one pound. Can they do this accurately and confidently? Can they use the appropriate language confidently, for example, *most expensive, cheaper, more than* and *less than*? Identify

any children who are hesitant or unsure and who, therefore, need further experience of this type. Check how the children handle the coins. Do they use the coins efficiently? Do they recognise, for example, that a 5 pence coin is more convenient than two 2 pence coins and one penny?

Opportunities for IT

As children add different items to the shop they could use a word processor to make labels. The activity would encourage children to use the number keys and they may need to be shown how to obtain the pound sign (£) by pressing SHIFT and the appropriate number key together. Children could also make posters for their shop using a word processor or art package.

Display ideas

Help the children make a poster for the shop detailing, for example, the cost of two books, three toys, how many things you can buy for less than one pound, the total cost of the three cheapest and dearest items, and so on.

Reference to photocopiable sheets

Photocopiable page 145 offers a list of prices which can be used as labels for the items in the shop.

CLASS CAFÉ

To be able to give change from one pound; to calculate change in a variety of ways.

†† *Four to six children.*

🕑 *30–40 minutes.*

Previous skills/knowledge needed

Children should know the addition and subtraction number bonds within 20. They should appreciate that there are 100 pence in one pound.

Key background information

This activity offers children the opportunity of giving change and can be used to encourage them to find the difference between two amounts in a variety of ways. For example, they might be asked what change should they give if 20 pence is offered for a 17 pence item. Starting at 17 pence, they would count forward to 20: 18, 19, 20.

This procedure could also be used to establish the difference in value between two amounts of money. For example, Joanna has 15 pence and Elaine has 11 pence; how much more has Joanna than Elaine?

Further dimensions might include counting on in jumps of 5 or 10 and counting back or moving towards the smaller number and counting the number of jumps, perhaps, on a number line. These methods are used here to help the learner calculate change in different ways.

Preparation

Prepare a class café offering a range of drinks and foods all priced less than one pound. Arrange tables and chairs appropriately. Make laminated copies of photocopiable page 146 and display them as menus around the café.

Resources needed

Copies of photocopiable page 146, toy food and drinks, toy money including 1p, 2p, 5p, 10p, 20p, 50p and £1 coins, number line.

What to do

Give each child a pound coin. Explain that they can each choose one item from the menu in the café. Discuss the fact that a one pound coin is the same value as 100 pennies. Get the children to take turns at being the café proprietor. Allow the children plenty of time to select their items and encourage them to explore ways of giving the correct change.

Discuss the strategies used by the group, and ask the children to demonstrate how they calculated the change from one pound. Encourage them to explain their methods for example: 'I bought a baked potato for 90p. I need to get change from one pound so the café owner can count on in ones, 91, 92, 93, 94, 95, 96, 97, 98, 99, 100. This means I get 10 pennies in change.' and 'The apple juice costs 45p. I need to get change from one pound so the café owner can count on in 10s first, and then 5p.'

Help the children to count back from one pound or 100p to the cost of the item. For example: 'The yoghurt costs

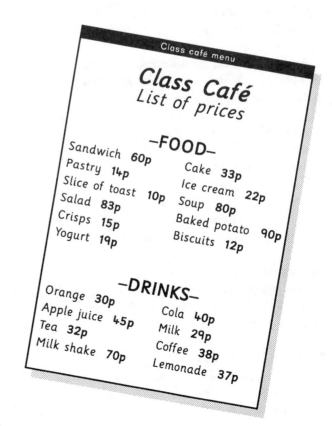

Class café menu

Class Café
List of prices

—FOOD—

Sandwich **60p**
Pastry **14p**
Slice of toast **10p**
Salad **83p**
Crisps **15p**
Yogurt **19p**

Cake **33p**
Ice cream **22p**
Soup **80p**
Baked potato **90p**
Biscuits **12p**

—DRINKS—

Orange **30p**
Apple juice **45p**
Tea **32p**
Milk shake **70p**

Cola **40p**
Milk **29p**
Coffee **38p**
Lemonade **37p**

19p. I can count back in 10s from 100 using the number line and counting the jumps: 90, 80 and so on to 20. This is 8 jumps and each jump is worth 10 pence; this is 80p and now I go back just one to 19. So the change is 81p.'

Encourage the children to compare the different methods. Discuss which one works best. Which one would be the quickest solution?

Help the children to appreciate the speed of counting in 10s, 2s and 5s, as appropriate. Start by giving change from one pound for a drink of cola costing 40p and a slice of toast costing 10p. Then proceed to items whose prices end in the digit 5, such as apple juice and crisps. Continue with items which allow the change to be calculated by counting in 10s, then 2s and so on.

Finally, get the children to compare the prices of different drinks and foods. Ask questions such as: 'How much more is the cola than the orange? How much more is the soup than the milk shake?' and so on. Encourage the use of the number line to calculate the difference and to help with counting on. Discuss which method of counting on they prefer and which method is the quickest.

Suggestion(s) for extension

Encourage the children to work in pairs to choose two or three items and give change from one pound.

Suggestion(s) for support

For this group, devise a similar cafe menu which has fewer items, all of which are multiples of 10. Teach the children to give change by counting on to one pound in 10s.

Assessment opportunities

Do the children understand how to count on in 10s, 5s, 2s and using a combination of these? How confidently do they handle this?

Opportunities for IT

Children could use a word processor to type and print menus for their café. They could experiment with different types and sizes of font to make the menu attractive. They could also be introduced to simple formatting commands, such as CENTRE to make an appropriate layout.

Older or more able pupils may be able to add simple pictures to the menu, either taken from clip art collections or drawn using a simple art package. Some of the menus could be printed as large copies which could be displayed on the café wall.

Reference to photocopiable sheets

Photocopiable page 146 offers children a price list which can be used in the main activity.

MULTIPLICATION AS REPEATED ADDITION

To be able to calculate multiplication sums using repeated addition in 2s, 5s and 10s.

†† *Four to six children.*

🕐 *30–40 minutes.*

Previous skills/knowledge needed

Children should know the addition and subtraction number bonds within 20.

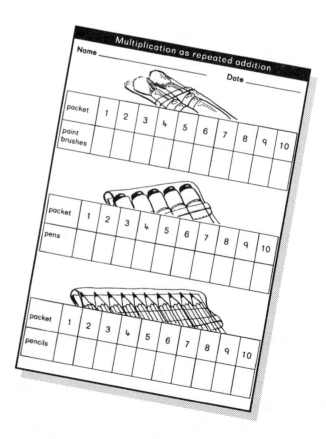

Calculations *and* problem solving

Key background information

This activity involves introducing children to the concept of multiplication through repeated addition. Children should be given plenty of practical experience in counting sets of objects, building up to using multiplication tables and understanding structure.

Multiplication notation can be introduced through such practical activities. The simple examples of multiplication as repeated addition described below are primarily to stimulate discussion between the teacher and pupils and between pupils themselves.

Preparation

Sort paintbrushes, pens and pencils into sets of 2, 5 and 10. If possible, put the sets into clear packets of the sort in which pencils etc. are sold. Alternatively, wrap them in clear plastic and seal the packets with adhesive tape. Make copies of photocopiable page 147 for each child.

Resources needed

Multiple packs of pens, pencils, paintbrushes and so on, copies of photocopiable page 147, paper and writing materials. For support activity: a number line, a collection of 2p, 5p and 10p coins, a selection of pictures of five-petalled flowers, animals with four legs, and so on. For extension activity: a calculator.

What to do

Begin by discussing the various packs of objects. Select paintbrushes, saying for example, 'This pack has 2 brushes. How many brushes will be in 2 packs? What about 3 packs?'

Allow the children time to respond to your questions. Ask them to explain how they worked out the problem.

Then show them 3 packs, and says to them: 'We can say that 3 packs have 2 plus 2 plus 2, which is 6 paintbrushes altogether. We can write this like this.' Write the number

sentence 2 + 2 + 2 = 6 on the board so that they can all see it. Ask: 'How could I work out how many paintbrushes there would be in 5 packs?

Give the children sufficient time to work out the problem. Keep the collection of packs on the table in case any children need to count out 5 packs. Once again, show the children how the number sentence can be written.

If necessary, give a few more example questions. ('How many paintbrushes in 6 packs? 7 packs?')

Go through a similar procedure with the packs of 5 and 10 objects. Encourage the children to pose their own questions as well as answer yours.

Next distribute copies of photocopiable page 147 to each child. Explain how to complete the tables, and work with them as a group on the first three boxes of each table.

As they are filling in the tables, encourage the children to explain how they are finding the number of paintbrushes, pens and pencils, for example: 'There are 3 packs of pencils. That means 10 pencils plus 10 pencils plus 10 pencils which makes a total of 30 pencils altogether. So 3 sets of 10 is 30.'

If necessary, let the children use the packs to help them work out the sums.

Help the children reflect further on what they are doing by sometimes asking questions such as: 'How big do you think the answer will be? Can you prove that your answer is correct?'

Throughout the activity, encourage the children to verbalise their thinking; ask them to explain what they are doing and how they obtain their answers.

Suggestion(s) for extension

Ask the children to think of their own examples of sets of objects to count.

Encourage them to work with larger numbers and to use a calculator to check their results. Challenge them to discover

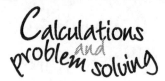

a quicker way of recording the results.

It is not necessary that they should use the multiplication sign, but they should be given the opportunity to apply their own strategies.

Suggestion(s) for support

Children may need extra support through further practical activities involving repeated addition of the kind in the main activity. Provide more objects for the children to count in sets, such as pictures of five-petalled flowers, animals with four legs, spiders and so on. The 0–100 number line could be used to illustrate 'jumping' in steps of the same size and provides a particularly valuable way of representing repeated addition.

Another useful approach would be to use 2p, 5p and 10p coins to represent the repeated addition.

Assessment opportunities

Note the children's responses to your questioning. Can they explain how they obtain answers? Are they able to use repeated addition confidently and accurately? Do they understand the notation used? Decide which children, if any, need further practice using concrete materials to demonstrate multiplication as repeated addition.

DIVISION AS SHARING

To begin to calculate division sums using objects; to begin to be able to deal appropriately with remainders.

†† *Four to six children.*

⏱ *30–40 minutes.*

Previous skills/knowledge needed

Children should know the addition and subtraction number bonds within 20. They should have lots of experience calculating multiplication sums using repeated addition.

Key background information

The early stages of division involve understanding the concept of division as sharing and division as repeated subtraction. The idea of sharing is the basis of this activity. It can be illustrated by asking the children to share a number of pens equally between two boxes. The aim of this request is to establish the idea that sharing involves putting one pen in each box, then another in each box, and so on so that, at the end, each box has the same number of pens.

Preparation

Prepare bags or packs of various objects, for example, biscuits, fruit, sweets, plastic cups, cutlery and so on. Make copies of photocopiable sheet 148 for children working on the extension activity and page 149 for children working on the support activity.

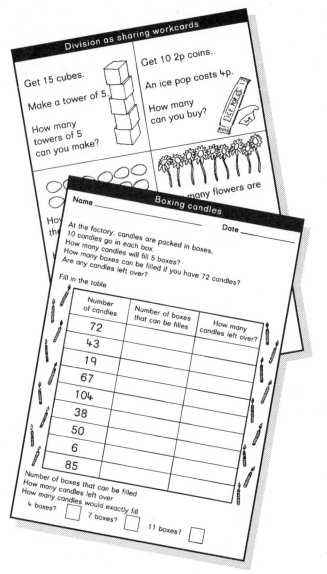

Resources needed

Packs containing different numbers of items, paper and writing materials. For extension activity: copy of photocopiable page 148. For support activity: copy of photocopiable page 149.

What to do

Ask one child to share, for example, 12 cups equally among the children in the group. Then discuss the process: 'How many cups did we have to share? How many did each get?' This activity should then be repeated with different numbers of objects to be shared. Discussion should establish that, for example, 20 biscuits were shared equally among five children and that each child got four biscuits.

Go on to sharing objects equally among children where there are 'left overs' or 'remainders'. Encourage discussion such as, 'We had 13 sweets. We shared them equally between six people. We each got 2 and there is 1 left over.'

Follow this by asking, for example, 'How many children can have 4 sweets from this packet containing 12?' Help them to work out the answer by removing 4 sweets and

Assessment opportunities
Note children's responses to your questioning. Do they understand the notion of sharing into equal groups? Can they use the terms 'left over' and 'remainder' appropriately? Do they understand the recording?

Reference to photocopiable sheets
Photocopiable sheet 148 provides a task for the extension activity. Photocopiable sheet 149 provides a task for the support activity.

THREE DICE ADDITION

To be able to estimate the answer to a simple addition sum.

†† *Pairs.*

🕐 *30 minutes.*

Previous skills/knowledge needed
Children should have a basic understanding of addition.

Preparation
Prepare a recording sheet similar to the one shown below or the children can draw up their own sheets as part of the lesson.

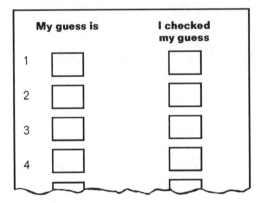

	My guess is	I checked my guess
1	☐	☐
2	☐	☐
3	☐	☐
4	☐	☐

giving them to the first child, then another 4 to the second and so on. When all the sweets have been removed help the group to count the number of children with 4 sweets. Discuss what happened, for example: 'We gave out 4 sweets each time and 3 people got 4. There are no sweets left for Amanda and Joe.'

Encourage children to say how many there were to share and how many had to be given out each time. Help them to recognise that 4 items were given out each time and that there are 3 lots of 4 sweets in the packet of 12.

Go on to discuss 'left overs', for example, 'We started off with 13 things. We tried to make groups of 3. We have 4 groups of 3 things and 1 left over.' Help children to record this information.

Finally, ask the children to work in pairs to make up problems involving sharing for another pair to solve. Let them use the packs of objects to help them to do the sharing if necessary. Ask them to record orally or in writing what they did.

Suggestion(s) for extension
Give pairs of children copies of page 148. Help the children interpret the task and get them to work together in pairs to complete it.

Suggestion(s) for support
Give pairs of children copies of page 149. Help the children interpret the task and let them work together on each one.

Resources needed
For each pair: three dice numbered 1 to 6 with figures rather than dots, two numerical dice (greater than six), a stopwatch or watch with a second hand, a calculator, two copies of a recording sheet (see above).

What to do
Give the pairs of children the three 1 to 6 dice and explain that one of them should throw the dice and estimate what the total score of the numbers shown would be. Since the aim is to estimate rather than calculate exactly, agree that the estimate must be given in, say, five seconds. Let the second child time the estimation process, and then record the estimate. If you have not provided preprepared sheets then encourage the children to think up their own design for a recording sheet. The second child should then use the

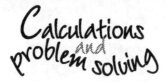
calculator to find the exact score and record it on the sheet. Encourage the children to discuss how accurate the estimate was.

Explain that the children should take turns throwing the dice, recording the guess, checking with the calculator, and recording the result. The value of this activity lies in the comparison of the estimate and the check.

Discuss the range of answers, saying, for example, 'Which estimate is very close? Which estimate is not so good?' and so on. Discuss the strategies they use to estimate. Encourage them to verbalise what they do to estimate quickly.

Discuss which are the most difficult combinations to estimate accurately, and ask the children to say why this is the case. Which combinations are easiest to estimate accurately? Why is this?

Next invite the children to do the same activity using two 1 to 6 dice and one dice marked from 6 to 12 (or greater). Ask them to fill in the results in the same way on the second recording sheet. Again discuss the strategies they use.

Finally, discuss with the children ways of deciding who the winner in each pair might be. On what basis could they decide this?

Suggest that the winning estimates should be those closest to the actual total.

Challenge them to consider a way of working this out using a calculator. Ask questions such as, 'Why should the person with the lowest difference win? Is it fair to decide who the winner is on the basis of one throw each?'

Allow them to make up their own rules. Discuss how fair these are in the whole group. Let them play applying their rules. Follow this by further discussion.

Suggestion(s) for extension
Use two or three of the higher numbered dice.

Spend some time discussing the strategies these children use to estimate the result.

Suggestion(s) for support
Use two dice instead of three.

Assessment opportunities
The recording sheet provides evidence of children's ability to estimate the answer to a simple addition sum. Consider the strategies they apply. Note their ability to discuss and try out strategies suggested by other people.

COUNTING ON AND ADDING ON

To recognise that counting on and addition provide a check on one another; to be able to use addition as a method for checking counting on.

†† *Pairs.*

🕑 *30 minutes.*

Previous skills/knowledge needed
Children should be able to do tasks involving one-to-one correspondence and they should understand ordinality.

Preparation
Copy photocopiable page 150 directly on to card or mount copies on to card. If possible, laminate or cover the card with clear adhesive plastic.

Make copies for each pair.

Resources needed
For each pair: a game board from photocopiable page 150, one numerical dice and one dot dice, counters, calculator.

What to do
Distribute the boards and counters. Give each pair a dot dice to start with. Explain to the children that the black cat and the white cat need to go home to their owners. They can only do this if the children throw the dice for them, count the number of dots and then move them that number of steps. Get the children to choose which cat to throw for, then let them play the game. Encourage them to explain what they are doing as they play.

Encourage them to consider other ways of moving along the path, asking questions such as, 'Is there a quicker way?

Counting on and adding on board game

Reference to photocopiable sheets

Photocopiable page 150 offers children a board game for this activity.

HOW MANY CUBES?

To recognise that calculations can be checked by reference to the original concrete situation.

†† *Pairs.*

🕐 *30 minutes.*

Previous skills/knowledge needed

Children should be able to do tasks involving one-to-one correspondence and they should understand ordinality.

Preparation

Make a recording sheet similar to the one shown below and make enough copies for the children to have one each. If required, the children can design and make their own recording sheets as part of the lesson.

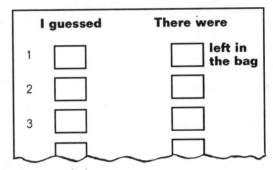

	I guessed	There were
1	☐	☐ left in the bag
2	☐	☐
3	☐	☐
	☐	☐

Resources needed

A recording sheet for each child (see above), a drawstring bag, a selection of cubes (or other counting apparatus).

If we add the number on the dice to the number where the counter is rather than counting on, will that be faster? Did anyone try doing it that way?'

Repeat the game using the numerical dice instead of the dot dice.

Help the children discuss the strategies they use. Invite them to discuss whether counting on or adding on is best and how one way might be used as a check on the other. Then let them play again with the player who throws the dice choosing whether to count on or add on, and the partner checking this by using the other method.

Finally, give each pair a dot dice, a numerical dice and a calculator. Ask them to play again totalling the two dice and using the calculator to aid the calculations.

Suggestion(s) for extension

Give the children two dice and ask them to play without the aid of a calculator. Ask them to consider all the possible combinations they can get by throwing two dice.

Suggestion(s) for support

Devise your own dice within a narrower range, for example, up to 3.

Assessment opportunities

Observe children as they play the game. Note what strategies they use and their confidence and willingness in trying out new ones. Are they able to use both counting on and addition and to use one as a check on the other?

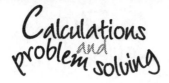

What to do

Ask one child in each pair to fill the bag with the appropriate number of cubes (depending on what number you want the children to work on).

Ask the second child to take out some cubes from the bag, showing the first child what has been removed, then ask the first child to estimate how many cubes are left. Check the estimate against the actual number of cubes left and get them to record both numbers. If you have not provided prepared recording sheets then encourage the children to design and make their own sheets. Let them take it in turn to play, each one recording their estimate and the actual number on their own recording sheet.

Discuss the strategies they use by asking questions such as, 'What helps you to know how many are left?' Encourage them to talk about the accuracy of their estimates: 'Which guess was very close? How do we know? Which number is the nearest to the number left in the bag? Is this a good guess?'

Finally, ask the children to consider how they would decide who in each pair was the winner. What would be a fair rule? How would you calculate the difference between the estimate and the check? Suggest that whoever has the lowest difference after each player has had a turn should be the winner.

Suggestion(s) for extension

Use a larger number of cubes. Encourage the children to estimate quickly by putting a limit of five seconds on how long they have to estimate the number of cubes. Encourage them to decide the fairest way to decide who the winner is. How would the difference be calculated?

Suggestion(s) for support

Use a clear plastic bag so that the children can see the remaining cubes as well as those removed from the bag. Encourage the children to discuss how they estimate. ('What do you have to notice or look carefully at?')

You might also need to reduce the number of cubes used in the activity.

Assessment opportunities

Observe the children as they play the game. Note what strategies they use. Have they grasped the idea of checking their estimates by going back to the bag and counting the cubes? Examine the evidence on the recording sheets.

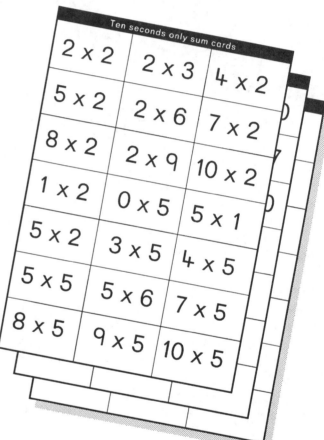

Ten seconds only sum cards

2 x 2	2 x 3	4 x 2
5 x 2	2 x 6	7 x 2
8 x 2	2 x 9	10 x 2
1 x 2	0 x 5	5 x 1
5 x 2	3 x 5	4 x 5
5 x 5	5 x 6	7 x 5
8 x 5	9 x 5	10 x 5

TEN SECONDS ONLY

To be able to check known multiplication facts on a calculator.

†† *Two to four children.*

🕒 *30 minutes.*

Previous skills/knowledge needed

Children should understand the process of multiplication.

Preparation

Make laminated card copies of photocopiable pages 151 to 153 and cut them up. Make enough copies for each group.

that are not answers to the sum cards. Award a score of one for each correct answer and deduct one for each wrong answer. Each time return the card to the table. Add some new cards to the game to make it more challenging.

Suggestion(s) for support
Play the game as above but confine the tasks to multiplying by 2. Gradually progress to multiplication by 5 and 10.

Assessment opportunities
Observe children as they play the game. Note their knowledge of these number bonds and their confidence in applying them. Observe them using the calculator to check their answers. Do they do this competently?

Reference to photocopiable sheets
Photocopiable pages 151 to 153 offer children sum cards with solutions and non-solutions.

CHECK YOUR JOURNEY

To be able to check addition through the use of subtraction.

†† *Two to four children.*

🕐 *30 minutes.*

Previous skills/knowledge needed
Children should understand the process of addition and subtraction.

Resources needed
For each group: cards from photocopiable pages 151 to 153, calculators, stopwatch or watch with a second hand.

What to do
Spread the sum cards on the table in front of the group and keep the solution cards yourself. Explain that you are going to call out a number (from your set of solutions) which will give an answer to one of the cards, and that the children can have 10 seconds in which to select the correct sum card. Explain that there are a few non-solution cards which do not have corresponding sums. Encourage the children to work out the answer to the sum using a calculator. If the answer matches the solution, the person who chose that card keeps it. The person with the most cards at the end is the winner.

Play the game several times, with the children taking turns at choosing a solution card. Collect up all the cards and put the sum cards and non-solution cards (i.e. 21, 13, 32, 36 and 73) to one side. Place the remaining solution cards in a pile on the table. Let the children take it in turns to select a card, and try to make up a multiplication sum to go with it. Encourage them to use the calculator to check the result. If it is right the child should keep the card, but if it is wrong the card should be put to the bottom of the pile. As before, the person with the most cards at the end is the winner.

Suggestion(s) for extension
Include the non-solution cards, i.e. call out some numbers

Calculations and problem solving

Preparation
Make card copies of photocopiable page 154 for each child.

Resources needed
For each child: copy of the recording sheet on photocopiable page 154, pencils and pens, chalkboard, calculator (optional for extension activity).

What to do
Explain to the children that they are going to go on number journeys. Show them an example by saying, 'Here are ways of getting from 2 to 10' and writing on the board:

2 + 1 + 2 + 2 + 1 + 2	=	10
2 + 8	=	10

Ask the children if they can find some more ways of making that journey? 'What is the shortest or the quickest journey from 2 to 10?'

Next help the children to think of ways of checking that

their journeys are correct. Suggest that they try subtraction, saying: 'You can begin at the end of your journey and take away all the way back to the beginning, for example, you can check this journey as follows:

2 + 1 + 2 + 2 + 1 + 2	=	10
10 − 2 − 1 − 2 − 2 − 1	=	2

Now find some ways of getting from 0 to 10; from 3 to 10; from 6 to 10; from 0 to 20; from 3 to 20; and from 6 to 20. Check your journeys by subtraction to make sure they are correct. Let the children use calculators to help them and encourage them to record their journeys on the recording sheet. Discuss the journeys with the children.

Suggestion(s) for extension
Encourage children to make up their own journeys. Invite them to use bigger numbers.

Suggestion(s) for support
Work with the children who need extra support. Help them to write down the number journeys from 2 to 10 and show them how to check them using subtraction.

Assessment opportunities
Observe children as they work. Decide whether they are able to check addition using subtraction. Do they do this competently? Note their knowledge of these number bonds and their confidence in applying them.

Display ideas
Collect the recording sheets and mount them on coloured paper. Make them into a booklet entitled 'Number journeys we made and checked.'

Reference to photocopiable sheets
Photocopiable page 154 offers children a recording card for this activity.

$2 + 1 + 1 + 1 + 1 + 1 + 1$

BROTHERS AND SISTERS

To be able to check addition through adding a set of data in a different order.

†† *Large group or whole class.*

🕐 *30 minutes.*

Previous skills/knowledge needed
Children should understand the process of addition and subtraction.

Preparation
None.

Resources needed
Chalkboard, paper and writing materials (optional).

What to do
Ask the children to state how many brothers and sisters they have. As they report the information, record it on the board as follows:

BROTHERS	SISTERS
2	2
1	1
3	2
1	5
2	1
3	4
1	0
2	3

Now ask the children to work out how many bothers children in the class have altogether by adding up the column of numbers. Next ask them to consider a way of checking that the total is correct. Encourage them to add the column of numbers from the opposite direction. Go through the same procedure with the 'sisters' column.

Finally, ask the children to work out how many brothers and sisters children in the group have altogether. Discuss different ways of finding out. Suggest that they add across the rows and total the new column. Discuss how they could check the result by adding in a different order. Help children to realise that a quicker way of finding out how many brothers and sisters altogether would be to add the two totals in the 'brothers' and 'sisters' columns.

Suggestion(s) for extension
Encourage children to generate their own data, for example, pocket money this week. Ask them to check it by adding in a different order.

Suggestion(s) for support
Arrange to have a smaller group than for the main activity, say a group of eight children. This will facilitate dealing with a smaller volume of information. Go through the same procedure as above. Again, the children should add the column of figures in different ways, for example, from the top down and from the bottom up. Discuss how this is a good way to check the accuracy of the result. Also emphasise that when adding numbers, the order in which you put or add the number makes no difference to the answer.

Assessment opportunities
Observe children as they work. Decide whether they are able to check their addition by adding in a different order. Do they do this competently and confidently? Note their knowledge of number bonds and their confidence in applying them.

Reference to photocopiable sheets
None.

MORE ADDING AND CHECKING

To be able to check addition through grouping data in more convenient sets.

✝✝ *Large group or whole class.*
🕓 *30–40 minutes.*

Previous skills/knowledge needed
Children should understand the process of addition and subtraction.

Preparation
None.

Resources needed
Paper and writing materials, chalkboard, large sheet of paper for each group on which to record their work, marker pens.

What to do
Generate real data from the children themselves, for example:
▲ how many books have members of the group (class) read this week?
▲ how many times in the week have they played a particular game?
▲ how much pocket money did they get this week?
▲ how many stars did members of the class get this week?
▲ how many times did they work on the computer this week?
▲ how many hours have they spent watching television?

As they report the information, record it on the board as follows:

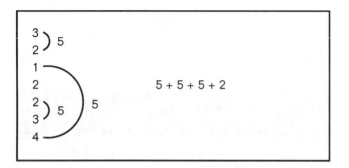

$5 + 5 + 5 + 2$

Now ask the children to look carefully at the data and find a way of grouping it which would make adding more convenient. Suggest that they try grouping in 5s. Discuss how this makes the adding more convenient but also offers a way of checking the addition. Highlight the fact that in adding the order does not matter.

Go on to examine other data sets in the same way, for example, the number of brothers and sisters of group or class members could be revisited (see the previous activity) and children could be invited to consider grouping this data set to make adding up more efficient and also to provide a check:

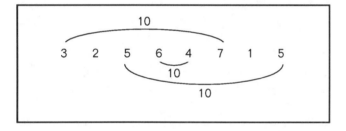

Discuss how it is convenient to group in 10s since there are several combinations which give 10. Add these first, then add on the 2 and the 1.

Provide some more examples to ensure children have grasped the idea of grouping data. Encourage them to examine the list of numbers carefully first to see combinations which can be added quickly and easily. Discuss why this is a good way of helping you to check the accuracy of your result.

Next ask the children to work in groups, to generate their own sets of data from within the group (if the group is large enough, i.e. five or more, otherwise allow them to include other class members in the data gathering process). Let them take turns to present this information on a chart or large sheet of paper. Encourage them to discuss ways of grouping and indicate these on the chart.

Suggestion(s) for extension
Encourage children to generate larger data sets and data sets with larger numbers, for example, their own school attendance records so far this month/year. Challenge them to group this data for adding and checking purposes.

Suggestion(s) for support
Arrange to have a smaller group than for the main activity, say a group of eight children. This will facilitate dealing with a smaller volume of information. Go through the same procedure as above. The children should be encouraged to look for patterns in the data, for example, same numbers. Discuss how grouping the numbers in different ways helps you to check your result. Also emphasise that when adding numbers, the order in which you put or add the number makes no difference to the answer.

Assessment opportunities
Observe children as they work. Decide first whether they understand the process of grouping data in more convenient ways. Then note whether they see the value of this as a checking device. Can they see patterns in data sets easily, for example, lots of combinations of 5, 10 and so on? Do they do this competently and confidently? Note their knowledge of number bonds and their confidence in applying them.

Reference to photocopiable sheets
None.

Handling data

Gathering and using information is something we do all the time insofar as we are processing and interpreting information around us in all sorts of ways. However, handling data in the classroom usually refers to the collection of quantitative (measured) or measurable information. It can be defined in terms of four activities, although all four need not be features of every data handling activity. These are questioning, collecting information, analysing the recorded information and interpreting the information.

The first is most important in that it dictates what information will be collected and has a bearing on how it will be recorded, how it will be analysed and what interpretations and conclusions will be drawn from it, for example: What are the most popular pets of people in the class/school? How good are we at skipping? What is the most common month for birthdays in our class?

The best sources of questions for children's data handling are their own everyday lives in and outside of school. One very fruitful source might be the class topic. The important thing to remember is that data handling should have a purpose and should be a response to some genuine question.

Lists, tables and charts are key sources of information in our daily lives, ranging from checking rail or bus journey timetables to comparing prices of similar items. We need to be able to extract information correctly and, when necessary, to construct lists, graphs or tables for our own use or for the use of others. Children's understanding of number can be greatly enhanced through the application of their numerical knowledge to situations involving the collection and interpretation of information. At the same time children learn to make sense of numerical information, to present and interpret information in a variety of formats and to see relationships within sets of data.

MAKING A DATABASE

Since data handling should be a response to a genuine question, the activities in this chapter are presented in the context of a theme (*ourselves*). The theme itself is typical of topics selected in an infant class as it provides opportunities for posing a range of questions that concern children's lives and experiences and for integrating a range of subjects. The theme is used as an example and the activities can be adapted to fit in with your own class topic.

Before embarking on the activities in this chapter, you need to collect a variety of information about the children in order to create a database from which they themselves can then extract information for analysis, presentation and interpretation. This database needs to contain a range of information about the children themselves. Each child should complete a questionnaire, perhaps as a follow-up to discussion about the topic and/or as a reading/writing activity. Questions should include things like:

▲ What is your name?

▲ What hobbies do you have?

▲ What subjects do you like best?

▲ How old are you?

You can provide lots of different or additional information, depending on the interests of the particular children.

It would be useful to put this class database on to a computer using simple database software. Depending upon the age and ability of the children, this could be done by the teacher in advance so that the database is ready to use or the teacher could set up the structure of the database and children enter their own information ready for later use by the class.

For younger children it is sensible to keep the number of different headings (fieldnames) small so that they are not overwhelmed by the amount of data. A mixture of numerical data and textual data is useful, particularly for later use in drawing graphs. You may not want to put in surnames unless you have several children with the same forename. Adding the sex of the child provides a useful starting point for discussions about how computers cannot tell the difference between boys and girls from the names.

If children are adding their own data, they are likely to need support, both to ensure that they know how to enter and edit their data and that they enter it correctly. This activity could be used to improve children's general IT skills, such as the use of the keyboard, cursor keys and mouse. Extra adult help can be useful here. Try to start this work in advance of actually needing to use the data as it could take several days to get every child to enter their data. You may also want to check the database through before you start to use it as extra spaces and full stops can affect the later use of the database. Make sure you save more than one version of the database so that if children alter or amend things you have another copy to use.

SORTING OURSELVES OUT

To be able to sort simple sets using one or two criteria.

†† *Large group or whole class.*

🕐 *30–40 minutes.*

Previous skills/knowledge needed

Children should have experience of sorting and classifying materials available in the classroom (shells, buttons, spools, beads, bricks, small toys, and so on) according to their own criteria. Through discussion with you they should be encouraged to say what they have done and why they have arranged the materials in that way.

Key background information

A set is a well-defined collection of objects. When asking children to sort out objects into sets, it is important that the specified criterion is clear and unambiguous. For example, the 'set' of children who are tall is ambiguous as there is no standard height by which to distinguish between people who are tall and people who are not tall. Consequently, there is no satisfactory attribute for forming a set.

In contrast, the set of children in the class wearing something with stripes or coloured blue is clearly defined: given any child in the class, it is possible to determine whether he belongs to that set.

Although the children will not need to use the terms *universal set* and *complement of the set*, these are useful concepts in developing understanding of sets.

The *universal set* refers to the entire set under consideration for a particular attribute, while the *complement of the set* refers to those objects which belong to the universal set but do not belong to the set for that particular attribute.

In order to develop further children's understanding of the concept of a set, as in the second part of the main activity here, it is better to encourage them to sort one collection of objects in two or three ways rather than in sorting two or three collections of objects in only one way. A carefully chosen collection of say, 10 to 15 objects, is more useful than a random collection of 30 objects.

Preparation
For this activity, arrange to work with a large group or whole class in the hall.

Resources needed
Skipping ropes and balls (3 or 4), mats, random sorting materials for the support activity, class database for the extension activity.

What to do
Begin the activity by referring to some aspect of the topic with which the children are already familiar, for example, birthdays and ages.

Remind the children that a set is a group of objects that belong together in some way by asking them to group themselves into different sets. Begin by telling the children that you want to make a set of children who are five (i.e. who have had their fifth birthday).

Those children who fall into this set should stand on a mat or another specified area.

Discuss the outcome, referring to those who are in the set *and* those who are not in the set. Ensure everyone understands the criterion or the attribute that is the reason that the children belong to each set: *these children have had/not had their fifth birthday.*

Continue sorting the children according to other criteria, for example:
▲ the set of children who walked to school today;
▲ the set of children who are wearing something red today;
▲ the set of children who are boys;
▲ the set of children who have brown eyes;
▲ the set of children who have a brother;
▲ the set of children who are wearing black shoes.

Each time refer to the set *and* those who are not in the set, stating what the criterion is. Help the children to

understand the concept by asking questions, for example: 'Why are particular children standing on the mat? Who is in the set of children wearing sandals today? In what way do these children belong together? Is there some way in which they are all the same? Who is not in this set? Why? Is there some way in which these are all the same?'

Proceed by selecting, say, three children from the whole group, according to some criterion, for example, wearing glasses, and ask them to stand together.

The children now have to work out what the criterion is, i.e. what they have in common, for example, all three children wear glasses.

Allow the children to select a set according to a secret criterion and then challenge the other children to state what it is. As appropriate, encourage them to notice when a set has more than one attribute in common. For example, the set of children wearing glasses is also the set wearing sandals.

Next divide the class into groups of say, six to eight. Give each group a skipping rope and a ball.

Explain that they can play some games to find out what different people in the group can do. (This may need to be handled with sensitivity.)

Begin by giving them some suggestions, for example: the set of children who can hop; the set of children who can skip; the set of children who can do five skips or more in one go; the set of children who can bounce the ball more than five times; the set of children who know particular games and so on.

Following this, ask them to sort themselves according to criteria of their own choosing.

Conclude the lesson by whole-class discussion on the sorting each group did. Refer to the attribute(s) used when sorting and *demonstrate* some of the sets according to the criteria used. Ask the children to explain why particular children belong to particular sets and encourage them to refer to more than one criterion as appropriate. For example, the set of children who can hop *and* do five skips.

A good way to finish the lesson is to select children to return to the classroom according to some criterion, for example, those wearing white socks first, followed by those wearing hairbands, those who collected up the equipment and so on. You could also let the children decide what the criteria are.

Suggestion(s) for extension
The children who need a greater challenge following the main activity could be asked to sort according to several criteria at once. For example, they could use the class database to find out the set of children whose favourite job in school is tidying the book corner *and* whose favourite hobby is reading stories *and* whose favourite colour is red. They should be encouraged to pose their own questions and find their own sets and talk about them.

Suggestion(s) for support
The children who found it very difficult to contribute to the main activity could be given further experience sorting and comparing random materials in sorting boxes filled with a variety of objects. Encourage them to discuss what they have done in the main activity using a wide range of vocabulary, for example: same, different; long, short; rough, smooth; round, flat; can roll, can't roll; and so on. Encourage them to apply this language themselves by showing them two objects, for example, two toy cars of a different colour, and ask them to say in which ways are they the same or different.

Following opportunity to observe and discuss, these children can work in pairs and sort, say beads, counters and cubes, as follows:
▲ the set of cubes, the set of beads, the set of counters;
▲ the set of objects that roll, the set of objects that do not roll;
▲ the set of objects that can be linked together, the set of objects that cannot be linked together;
▲ the set of yellows, the set of blues.

Encourage the children to discuss their sorting as they work using questions such as: 'Why do these objects go together? Why does this object not belong?'

Assessment opportunities
Note individual children's responses to the questions you ask. Do they know why particular people are grouped together? Are they able to use the language appropriately? Do they do this confidently? Identify children who find it difficult to work out your criteria and who, therefore, need further experience of this type.

Opportunities for IT
Once children have undertaken the physical sorting activities they might like to use their computer database to ask the same questions. This would involve setting up a simple search like:

> **find the names of all the boys:**
> *search for sex includes boys and print their names*
> **find the children who have a brother:**
> *search for brothers/sisters includes brothers and print their names*

On a second or third session the computer database could be introduced alongside the physical sorting process so that the two sets of information can be compared. This would give an opportunity for the class group to be shown how to use the computer database and to print out the answers.

This simple search is equivalent to sorting out a set of children. Indeed many computers refer to the answer as a sub-set of the full set of information. If there are children's names missing from the database, this should be explored so that children come to realise the importance of asking the correct question and the need for accuracy in entering data.

You may need to introduce the term search for these activities as computers reserve the word sort for arranging data into numerical or alphabetical order. For example, you could tell the children that they are going to search out the set of children with blue eyes. More able children could be introduced to a simple 'and' search which looks for a set of children based on two criteria; for example:

> **children with blue eyes and blonde hair:**
> *search for eyes includes blue and hair includes blonde and print out the names*
> **girls with brown eyes:**
> *search for sex includes girls and eyes includes brown and print out the names*

Display ideas
Set up a display of sets of coloured objects contained within appropriately coloured PE hoops. Make labels describing the sets' attributes.

SORTING USING CARROLL DIAGRAMS

To be able to sort objects using Carroll diagrams.

†† *Whole class followed by group work in threes or fours.*

🕐 *30–40 minutes.*

Previous skills/knowledge needed

Children should understand the notion of a set.

Key background information

There are several ways of recording sorting activities.

Two common ways of representing the sorting process are the Carroll and Venn diagrams. The Carroll diagram, invented by Lewis Carroll, author of *Alice in Wonderland*, divides a set into at least two categories, for example:

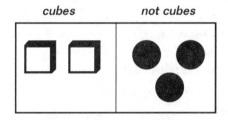

The above example involves sorting by one criterion. The Venn diagram, consists of an outer rectangle and at least one circle, for example:

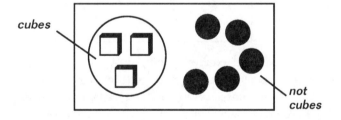

It is important that the outer rectangle is included in a Venn diagram. To avoid confusing the children, only the Carroll diagram is used in this activity.

The activity involves representing the following information: the children in the class who can ride a bike/can't ride a bike and the children who have/have not got a pet. It is important to ensure that no value judgements are attached to the results of the activity.

It goes on to combine this information on one chart. However, you may decide this is too much for one lesson in which case the combining part could be done at a later stage.

Preparation

Arrange for children to work as a whole class or large group first, then in groups of three or four. Ensure each group has access to the class database.

Resources needed

For the class activity or large group activity: class database; flipchart, two sets of labels with children's names, Blu-tack. For the small group, follow-up activity: class database, paper and writing materials, different coloured beads and cubes (or other sorting materials) for the support activity.

What to do

Introduce the activity by discussing different characteristics of the class as a whole, for example: 'We are all in class one. There are 29 children in this class. We are very good at reading in this class.'

Relate the discussion, as appropriate, to other work the children may have done within the topic 'Ourselves'. Go on to discuss things the children may not know (but have access to) about each other, for example, who in the class/group can ride a bike.

Encourage the children to consider ways of representing this information. Distribute the labels. Draw a Carroll diagram on the flipchart.

can ride a bike	can't ride a bike yet

Ask the children to stick their names on the diagram in the appropriate space, and ask questions such as, 'Who can ride a bike? How can we tell this from the diagram?'

Discuss the results.

Choose another criterion, for example owning a pet, and repeat the process.

has a pet
Ann
does not have a pet
Jade   Shelly

Again, ask questions such as, 'Who has a pet? How do we know from the diagram?'

Next, ask the children if they can find out who can ride a bike and has a pet. How could this information be put on one chart?

An example would be as follows:

	can ride	can't ride
has a pet		
does not have a pet		

81

Help them interpret the result by asking the following questions:

▲ Who can ride a bike and has a pet?
▲ Who can ride a bike but does not have a pet?
▲ Who are the children who do not have pets?

Encourage the children to make up questions about the chart to ask others in the group. Discuss other information the class would like to know about each other, for example, who can/can't swim, can/can't knit and so on.

Now ask the children to work in groups of three or four. Give each group a copy of the class database. Tell each group that they should analyse a different piece of information from the database which can later be displayed in the classroom on a Carroll diagram.

If appropriate, the groups could combine two skills on to the one chart, for example, swimming and knitting. Encourage the children to share and discuss their results as they work and draw their attention to any empty sets.

Finally, display all charts produced by the groups and discuss these in the large group setting. Encourage the children to ask questions to children in other groups.

Lots of discussion should be encouraged to assist the interpretation of the diagrams.

Suggestion(s) for extension

The children who are ready for a greater challenge could be asked to sort their classmates according to their favourite hobbies. First, each child in the group should list four hobbies which they think are the most popular, for example: swimming, riding a bike, listening to stories, watching TV. Ask them how many children in the class do they think would choose that

particular hobby. Tell the children to record this information on a Carroll diagram.

Favourite hobbies of children in our class - our estimates			
Swimming	Cycling	Listening to stories	Watching TV
6	12	6	7

Having first estimated the answers and recorded them on a Carroll diagram, the children can then find out who likes what best and say which is really the most popular hobby in the class. They will need access to the class database to do this.

Suggestion(s) for support

Children needing extra support might need to be taken through the main activity again in a smaller group, using their own names.

To reinforce the notion of recording using a Carroll diagram, it might be helpful to play a game on each sorting and recording event. With the children working in pairs ask them to sort objects into two sets, for example, things that are yellow/not yellow and things that roll/do not roll:

	yellow	not yellow
can roll		
can not roll		

Ask one child to remove secretly an object from a cell in the Carroll diagram. The child must then show it to her partner who should then describe where it has come from and replace it in the correct place. If the child places the object correctly she is given a point. They continue to play, taking it in turns to guess, until one of them gets six points.

Assessment opportunities

Note individual children's responses to the questions you ask. Do they appreciate the sorting and recording procedure? Are they able to use the language appropriately and confidently? Can they make and interpret the diagrams done by their own group and the other groups? Which children can make and interpret diagrams involving two criteria? Identify children who may need extra experience of these activities.

Opportunities for IT

Children could use the class computer database to search out information to be displayed in the Carroll diagrams. They would need to search for:

which children's favourite hobby is swimming?
search for hobby includes swimming
which children's favourite hobby is watching TV?
search for hobby includes watching TV

Children could also tackle the question by sorting the computer database on the hobbies field. If the list is sorted by hobbies into alphabetical order all of the swimming children will be grouped together and it will be easy to count up the names. You might even challenge the more able children by asking them to use the computer database to find out which is the most popular hobby in the class.

Display ideas
Display the completed Carroll diagrams in the classroom where children can refer to them in cross-curricular work and other work on data handling.

TALLYING

To be able to use tallying when collecting data.
Large groups or whole class then small groups.
30 minutes.

Previous skills/knowledge needed
Children should be able to count in fives.

Key background information
In recording the number of times an event occurs, children should be introduced to methods of tallying. Here are two:

Event (Our Pets)	Tally	How many times
Dogs	₦₦ II	12
Cats	₦ I	6
Hamsters	IIII	4
Rabbit	II	2

Event (Our Pets)	Tally	How many times
Dogs	◻ ◻ ∟	12
Cats	◹ I	6
Hamsters	◻	4
Rabbit	∟	2

Preparation
Arrange to work with a large group or whole class to demonstrate one or two ways of tallying.
Then children should be able to work in small groups.

Resources needed
Flipchart (optional), for each group: class database.

What to do
Begin this activity by referring to any previous work done on the topic 'Ourselves'.

With the large group or whole class begin to extract information about the class from the database, for example, the different ways the children usually travel to school. List the various means of travelling (car, taxi, bus, train, walk) on the board or flipchart. Then tell the children that you want to find out how each of them came to school that morning. For each response place a tick in the corresponding column as follows:

Walk	✓✓✓
Train	✓✓✓
Bus	✓✓✓✓✓
Taxi	✓✓✓✓✓
Car	✓✓✓✓✓✓✓✓✓✓✓

Once the chart is finished, total up the number in each column and write the number at the end of each row. Draw the children's attention to the difficulty of counting each tick and how easy it is to make a mistake.

Introduce them to the concept of tallying. Explain to them that tallying is a way to ensure that information is accurately recorded and that it is a more efficient way of recording than counting ticks.

Repeat the survey but this time use one of the forms of tallying indicated above. Can the children see that tallying makes it easier to see how many children use the different ways of travelling to school?

Next ask the children to work in groups and to find out one piece of information about members of the class from the class database, for example:
▲ favourite chores in school;
▲ pets people in the class have;
▲ favourite foods of class members;
▲ favourite drinks of class members;
▲ ages of children in the class.

Give each group access to the class database and then let the children use the information to make up their own tally charts. They will need to organise themselves so that each member of the group gets a turn at doing the tallying.

Finally, the children should come together as a class with the teacher to discuss their results and how they did their tallying.

Suggestion(s) for extension
Some children could be encouraged to set up a constant on the calculator so that each press of the calculator represents another five responses. Do this by keying in (5)(+)(+)(=). Each time (=) is pressed another 5 is registered.

Suggestion(s) for support

To help those who have difficulty with tallying, you might use Unifix cubes or beads on a string which could be grouped into sets of 5. This can help to make the process more concrete and experimental.

Assessment opportunities

Observe the children as they do the tallying. Do they know how to do it? Ask them why it is a good idea. Refer to the recording sheet as evidence of their ability to use tallying.

Opportunities for IT

If the computer database contains a wide range of information, it can be used to produce a smaller printed set of information for children to use for tallying.

Children could reinforce their database skills by checking their tallying answers against the computer database. They will need to discuss how to get the information from the database, as it is impossible to set up a single search which identifies the ages of the children in class directly. This could be done by sorting on age so that children are ranked in order and the number in each group counted, or by making a number of searches looking for children of a specific age, for example:

> **children who are 5?**
> *search for age equals 5*
> **children who are 6?**
> *search for age equals 6*

A pie chart will usually yield this information directly but may be beyond the experience of most children at this age.

RECORDING USING A TWO-WAY TABLE

To be able to present simple data in a two-way table.

✝✝ *Large groups or whole class.*

🕐 *30–40 minutes.*

Previous skills/knowledge needed

Children need to have had experience of sorting objects into sets.

Key background information

Data can be presented on a two-way table, for example, favourite colours of members of the class broken down by gender:

	Blue	Pink	Green	Yellow
Boys	2	2	11	9
Girls	2	1	10	4

or items of clothing by the patterns on them:

	T-shirt	Scarf	Hat
Spots			
Stripes			
Zig-zag			

Preparation

Arrange to work with the whole class or a large group first, then to work in small groups. Prepare name tags and a large sheet of paper or card, divided into the categories you intend to use.

Task / Name	Washing the paint pots	Checking the science equipment	Tidying the book corner
Surinder			
Sam			

Resources needed

For each group: class database, large sheet of card, name tags, Blu-tack, paper, writing materials.

What to do

Tell the children that you want to organise the chores in the classroom and so you need to find out each person's favourite job.

Ask each child in the group to tell you which jobs they like best and record it on the two-way table.

Task / Name	Washing the paint pots	Checking the science equipment	Tidying the book corner
Surinder	✓	✓	
Sam		✓	
Jamie			✓
Anna	✓		
Ben	✓		✓
Zoe		✓	

When the information is presented on the two-way table, help the children to interpret the diagram. Can they name the boys who like tidying the book corner? Who likes washing the paint pots and tidying the book corner? Which girls like checking the science equipment?

Draw the diagram again but this time instead of writing the names of the children put in the numbers of girls and boys who like each chore best.

Favourite jobs of boys and girls in this class			
	Washing the paint pots	Checking the science equipment	Tidying the book corner
Boys	3	2	1
Girls	1	2	5

Discuss the preferences of girls and boys as follows: 'What do most boys in this group like? Which job do most girls like? How do the girls and boys differ in the jobs they like doing in this class?'

Extend the discussion by posing such questions as: 'Supposing no boys liked checking the science equipment – how would we show this information?' Encourage the children to appreciate that there would be a zero in the last column of the first row.

Next help the children to ask questions about other information they have collected about themselves, for example favourite foods, favourite drinks, favourite colours. The intention should be to find out if certain groups of children, for example, dark haired/light haired, older children/younger children, girls/boys like the same food/drinks/colours.

Questions they might consider in advance might be: 'Will more girls than boys like chips? Will children born in the winter like the same foods as children born in the summer?'

They should construct their own two-way tables, writing in the names and/or the numbers in each cell.

Finish the lesson by encouraging each group to explain to the rest of the class what they have found out.

Suggestion(s) for extension
Let the children look at the information presented in other two-way tables for example, bus or train timetables, the school timetable for, say, using the PE hall. Make sure that these tasks are given some useful purpose so that the

information which the children need to extract from the tables is set in a context.

Suggestion(s) for support
It is vital that children have a purpose for constructing the table so that the information given has a real meaning. Also children can be helped to understand by an adult prompting questions such as 'Do you think that ...?' or 'How many children like ...?'

This might be achieved in a small group setting following the above discussion and demonstration with the large group or whole class.

Assessment opportunities
Refer to the recordings that the children make as this provides evidence of their ability to present information on a two-way table. Note also the children's responses to your questioning, especially in relation to the interpretation of the table. Can they read the table and extract the relevant information?

Opportunities for IT
Children could use the class computer database to search for the same information. The activity could be used to highlight effective use of IT for handling larger amounts of data. Two groups of children could be given the same task and one allowed to use the computer and the other the paper database. Providing children's computer skills are reasonable there will come a point when the amount of data to be searched makes a computer database faster and more reliable.

You may also like to use this work to focus children's attention on computer databases used outside the classroom. Most children will be familiar with the library, or you could talk about the telephone directory database, or how a bank keeps information about its customers. You might also like to talk about the need for accurate information. What happens when the operator at the library forgets to tell the database you have returned your book?

Display ideas
Ask each member of each group to write one sentence about the table. All tables and interpretations of them could be added to the class database or made into a class book and put on display.

BLOCK GRAPHS

To be able to present data in a simple block graph; to be able to interpret data presented in a simple block graph.

†† *Large group or whole class.*

🕐 *30–40 minutes.*

Previous skills/knowledge needed
Children should understand the notion of a set.

They should have had lots of experience of sorting and recording using Venn or Carroll diagrams (see 'Sorting using Carroll diagrams' on page 81).

Key background information
Pictograms communicate information in a pictorial form. They can be used to show similar information to a simple block graph, although they normally have a key. In block graphs each occurrence is shown as a separate unit or block. To find out the number of occurrences you count the blocks. Bar charts show the number of occurrences by the height of the bar.

Preparation
Arrange to work with a large group of children.

Resources needed
Two large sheets of card and markers for you to demonstrate the different methods of representing the information, paper and colouring materials for the children to draw pictures of themselves, gummed paper.

What to do
Begin the lesson by a discussion of the topic 'Ourselves' to ensure that the children have a context for presenting some information about themselves. This discussion should be linked to any previous work the class has done on tallying and on presenting information in two-way tables.

Prepare children for presenting information in a block graph by firstly providing experience of making pictograms. Ask each child to draw and cut out a small picture of themselves on gummed paper. Ask them to select some aspect of information about themselves, for example, age. Use the class database to check the ages of the children or ask each child to say whether they are five, six or seven years old. As they respond, help them to stick their picture on to the relevant column of the graph.

Pictogram to show...

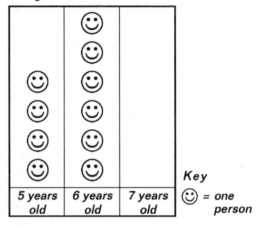

Once the children have stuck their pictures in the appropriate place on the graph discuss the results by asking questions which encourage the interpretation of the pictogram for example: 'How many people are five, six, seven? What age are most people in the class?'

Next demonstrate to children how to present this information in a different way. Instead of putting in a picture, shade one square of the grid.

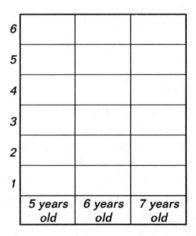

Discuss the results to ensure that everyone understands how to interpret the information. Help them to appreciate that the same information has been presented here as was given in the pictogram but in a different way.

Next help the children to present further information about the class as block graphs, for example, our favourite pets, drinks, colours and so on. When each group has completed a block graph, encourage them to say or write four things about the graph. For example, 'Most people in our class are six years old. No one is seven years old. Four people are five years old. We have nobody who is four years old.' Share and discuss the results in the larger group.

Encourage children to ask questions of each other.

Suggestion(s) for extension

Encourage children to go on to present information on a bar chart. For example, this chart shows the number of children in each class who usually come to school by car:

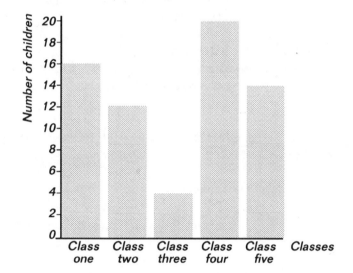

They could also create some questions about their graphs to ask each other.

Suggestion(s) for support

Children needing extra support should be given further opportunities to discuss:
▲ what information is needed and why;
▲ their interpretations of the block graphs;
▲ how the completed graphs can be used.

Assessment opportunities

Note individual children's responses to the questions you ask. Do they realise that the same information can be presented in different ways? Are they able to use the language appropriately and confidently? Can they make and interpret the pictographs and the block graphs? Identify children who may need extra experience doing these activities.

Opportunities for IT

Although children need the experience of drawing their own

graphs using paper and pencil, they should also be introduced to graphing software on a computer. This will enable them to draw graphs more quickly, and to experiment with a range of graphical types.

The computer database will have some graphing facilities which will enable children to draw block graphs of the searches they have created. With support, younger children might like to use graphing software to draw pictograms using a range of predetermined pictures and block graphs.

Whichever technique is used, children should be focused on the need to interpret their graphs, answering simple questions and discussing how easy it is to understand what the graph says. One advantage of using the computer is that it is often possible to rearrange graphs to give a clearer picture of the data, so that, for example, favourite pets can be displayed in descending or ascending numerical order.

Once children have become proficient at using the computer database and drawing graphs they could be given the task of displaying information from the class database itself. For example, they could be asked to draw a graph showing the colour of children's eyes in the class. They should also be asked to explain what their graph shows.

It would be useful to discuss with children the advantage of using the computer to draw graphs in this way. They might suggest a number of answers which will show that they are gaining some understanding of the benefit of using IT:
▲ it is quicker;
▲ they can try out different graphs easily;
▲ they can correct mistakes;
▲ work is more accurate;
▲ work looks better.

Display ideas

Ask each group to write four sentences or four questions (for the reader to answer) about their block graphs and display them with the graph.

USING A SCALE

To be able to present data in a graph using a simple scale on one of the axes; to be able to interpret data presented in a graph using a simple scale on one of the axes.

†† *Large group or whole class.*

🕒 *30–40 minutes.*

Previous skills/knowledge needed

Children should have had a lot of experience of sorting and recording using Venn or Carroll diagrams (see 'Sorting using Carroll diagrams' on page 81). They should have had a lot of experience presenting and interpreting data on pictograms and on block graphs. They should understand the process of division.

Preparation

Collect information involving a large amount of data, for example, the number of people in each class in the school (or several classes) who usually eat dinner in school or the number of children in each class (or several classes) in the school who usually travel to school by car.

Resources needed

Large sheets of card, markers, flipchart, paper and writing materials.

What to do

Begin by referring to the topic 'Ourselves' and provide a reason for presenting the relevant information, for example the number of children who eat dinner in school.

Use the board or a flipchart and divide it into, say, a 5 X 5 grid. Begin to record the information which you have collected, for example the number of people in five classes who usually eat dinner in school. The children will quickly discover that the grid is too 'small' to accommodate it. Discuss possible solutions such as using smaller boxes or letting each box stand for more than one child. Decide to try the second option. Discuss how the axis might be labelled if each box stood for two children.

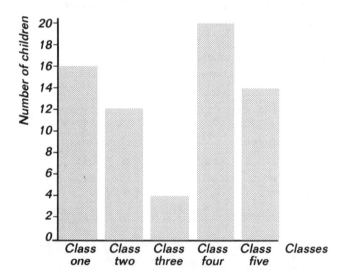

Help the children to present the information using each square to represent two children. Discuss how by doing this fewer squares or boxes are needed. Let the children complete the graph using this scale.

Discuss the results, ensuring that each member of the group understand that now each box or square stands for two children rather than just one child: 'How many children from class one usually eat dinner in school? How do we know?'

To challenge the children further, ask them to consider other possible scales: 'What about having each square stand for three people? Would this be a good idea? Why? Why not? How would the graph change if each square stood for

four people? Would we use up as many squares as before? What would you have to do to make sure everyone knew how we made the graph?'

Refer to the fact that numbers on one of the axes change but that the names on the other axis remain the same. Why is this so?

Next ask the children to form groups of four or five and distribute the same information to each group, for example, the number of children in several classes who come to school by car. Encourage them to present this information on a graph where each box stands for two children. Alternatively, encourage them to make up their own scale. Help them to compose a brief interpretation of the graph, for example: Class 4 has the most people who come to school by car; Class 3 has the least; 67 people altogether come to school by car.

Conclude the lesson by sharing and comparing the completed graphs and interpretations.

Suggestion(s) for extension

Encourage those who are ready for a further challenge to present continuous data using a scale, for example, the height of children in the class. They will need access to the class database. They will have to decide what variable goes on each axis, i.e. number of children and height. They will have to decide what interval to use in presenting the heights.

Suggestion(s) for support

Help children to appreciate scale by placing a two pence coin in each square. This and the follow-up discussion can help to reinforce the notion of one square standing for two people.

Assessment opportunities

Note individual children's responses to the questions you ask. Do they appreciate the need for a scale? Are they able to decide what the scale should be (with your support)? Can they make and interpret the scale graphs? Identify children who may need extra experience doing these activities.

Opportunities for IT

Most of the computer software used with younger children will scale graphs automatically to fit on the screen and on the printout. This will sometimes mean that graphs are not easy to read, particularly when larger amounts of data are used. With some software the computer will even decide how to group data into sets for display. You might like to talk to children about some of the graphs they have produced using the computer and discuss how the computer has sorted out the scale.

Display ideas

During whole-class discussion, decide on four or five sentences which describe the graph well. Display these with the graph.

Assessment

The National Curriculum demands that teachers' own professional judgement play a greater role than ever in informing teaching and learning. Assessment retains a pivotal role in the mathematics curriculum. Effective assessment in mathematics, as in any area of study, could be said to be at the heart of good teaching and learning for it identifies strengths and weaknesses and points to means of overcoming the latter through the former. It can provide reliable and valid information on pupil progress and can help the pupils themselves in taking their learning forward.

Teachers are already well aware of the many purposes of assessment: diagnostic/formative, summative, evaluative, etc. Within the activities in this book, formative assessment opportunities have been identified within most lesson plans. The activities suggested in this chapter are designed to support the teacher in summarising achievement in number at the end of the key stage. This end-of-key stage assessment may be used, therefore, to support the updating of teacher assessment levels. It assists the teacher in making a more global assessment of achievement which could be used for purposes of reporting to parents and to other colleagues.

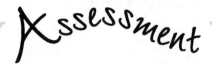

USING THE ACTIVITIES

In order to remember the responses of the child and the learning demonstrated together with the context of the assessment, some recording system is necessary. A suggestion for a grid is offered to support the teacher in recording key aspects of the assessment in relation to individual children, for example, whether and when elements have been understood.

While there are obvious implications for assessment throughout all the activities detailed in the previous chapters, the purpose at this stage is to offer short, teacher-directed activities which focus on particular number objectives or a cluster of objectives. The primary aim is to assess learning, although the activities themselves also provide for learning-oriented interaction with the child, and depending on the activity, between children themselves. For efficiency and manageability, the activities are designed so that several learning objectives can be assessed through the one task. Guidance is offered on what to look for and how to interpret the outcomes.

From the child's point of view the modes of assessment incorporated into these summative activities include: carrying out tasks using concrete materials set by you, the teacher; carrying out tasks without the aid of concrete materials; solving problems; discussing ideas; responding to instructions; recording results/solutions to problems.

From the teacher's point of view, the styles of assessment involve: setting up particular tasks with built in checking up procedures; questioning; listening; observation.

COUNTING THE ANIMALS

Counting; recognition of number symbols 0–10(20); matching sets according to the number of items contained in them; comparing sets and using the language of comparison, for example, less than, more than; understanding and using the language of ordinal number; recognising odd and even numbers.

†† *Group of three children.*
🕐 *15–20 minutes.*

Key background information

Up to three children could be assessed together in this activity. A recording sheet can be used for up to three children (as shown in the illustration). You should use this to record the evidence as you go along and to make comments if appropriate.

The demands of this activity are in line with the requirements for Level 1, but please note that addition and subtraction and pattern work are not included in this activity. The activity assumes the use of numbers 0–10, but this can be adapted to assess numbers from 0–20 if preferred.

Preparation

Photocopy page 100 and cut out the numbers. Photocopy pages 98 and 99 and cut out the pictures. The pictures and numbers can be mounted on to card and laminated if necessary.

Aspect of assessment	PoS	Evidence and outcomes	Name of child/ Date	Name of child/ Date	Name of child/
Counting.	2(a)	Did the child count the sets of animals reliably?			
Understanding and using the language of ordinal number.	5(a)	...order the animal cards correctly? ...identify the sets with the largest and smallest numbers?			
Matching sets according to the number in them.	4(d)	...recognise and use correctly the terms 'more than' and 'less than'?			
Recognise sequences including odd and even numbers.	2(a)	...recognise and identify sets with even and odd numbers of animals?			
Matching sets according to the number in them.	4(d)	...match the number and animal cards correctly?			
Recognition of number.	2(b)	...read the numbers correctly?			
Understanding the language of ordinal number.	2(a)	...sequence the numbers correctly?			
Checking results.	2(b)	...check the result by matching correctly the numbers and concrete materials?			

Resources needed

Photocopiable pages 98 and 99 (animal cards) – one set for each child, photocopiable page 101 (number cards 0–10) – one set for each child, collection of cubes or counters.

What to do

Provide each child with a set of animal cards from photocopiable pages 98 and 99. Ask the children to count how many animals are on each card. Select different cards for each child, then invite them to sequence the animal cards according to the number of animals on them, beginning with the lowest number.

Ask them to pick out the following cards:
▲ the one with the largest number;
▲ the one with the smallest number;
▲ a number larger than 5;
▲ larger than 6 but smaller than 10 and so on.

Mix up the cards and now invite the children to sequence them again according to the number of animals on them, but this time beginning with the highest number. Observe how confidently each child goes about this task. Are they dependent on what others in the group do or are they able to work independently? Next ask them to find a card containing an even number of animals. Encourage them to explain how they know it has an even number. Responses might include: the animals can be paired, put in twos; there isn't one left over when you pair them; 2, 4, 6, 8 and 10 are even numbers. In the same way ask them to identify a card containing an odd number of animals.

Provide each child with a set of number cards from photocopiable page 101. Ask them to match the number cards to the corresponding animal card.

Ask the child to name each number card and then to arrange them in numerical order, starting with the lowest and working towards the highest number. Collect up all the cards again and reshuffle one set of the number cards and place them on the table, face down. Ask one child to remove, say, three cards and then let the child who is being assessed sequence the remaining cards and to decide which numbers are missing.

Ask the child to pick out the following cards:
▲ largest number;
▲ the smallest number;
▲ a number larger than 5;
▲ larger than 2 but smaller than 6 and so on.

Ask them to check the result using counters.

Ask the children to sort the numbers into odd and even, then discuss the results with you. Note whether individuals have attained the skills and understanding necessary to complete these tasks successfully using the recording grid. You might want to note down whether the child concentrated well, understood your instructions, was motivated, and so on.

Reference to photocopiable sheets

Photocopiable page 101 gives a set of number cards from 0–10 and photocopiable pages 98 and 99 provide a set of animal cards.

THREE-DIGIT NUMBERS

Recognition and writing of two and three-digit numbers; ordering sets of three and four-digit numbers according to their value; recognition of the significance of the position of a digit in a number for its value.

†† *Small group of up to three children.*

🕐 *15–20 minutes.*

Key background information

Up to three children could be assessed together in this activity, using a recording sheet similar to the one shown in the illustration. This sheet suggests questions to focus the assessment, the answers to which provide the evidence of performance. You should refer to the questions to record the evidence as you go along and make comments if appropriate. The demands of this assessment activity are in line with the requirements for work regarding place value for Level 2.

You might want to modify this task to make it less or more demanding. You could do the task using two-digit numbers only; this would be in line with Level 1 work. You could extend the demands to Level 3 by using four-digit numbers and following the same procedure.

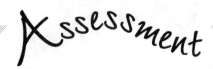

Aspect of assessment	PoS	Evidence and outcomes	Name of child/ Date	Name of child/ Date	Name of child/ Date
Recognising the significance of position for the value of a number.	2(a)	Did the child make the largest number possible from the three digits?			
Recognising the significance of position for the value of a number.	2(a)	...the smallest number possible from the three digits?			
Recognising the significance of position for the value of a number.	2(a)	Can the child explain how one number is bigger/smaller than another?			
Recognising and writing 2- and 3-digit numbers.	2(b)	Does the child recognise the significance of position of digits for the value of a number?			
Recognising the significance of position for the value of a number.	2(a)	Did the child correctly identify the digit in the number which signifies the highest value?			
Ordering 2- and 3-digit numbers according to value.	2(b)	...sequence the numbers in order of value?			
Recognising sequences including odd and even numbers.	2(b) 2(a)	...correctly identify odd and even numbers? ...know how to recognise an odd/even number?			

Preparation

Photocopy page 100 and cut out the numbers 0–9. Arrange for children to work as a small group and arrange to assess one or two children.

Resources needed

Photocopiable page 100 (numbers cards 0–9), paper and writing materials for recording.

What to do

Provide each child with a set of any three numbers from 0–9. Explain that you want them to make up as many three-digit numbers as possible from these three cards. They should record all their numbers on paper.

Discuss the results with each child individually. What is the biggest number that can be made? What is the smallest number? Why?

Can they explain that the position of the digits in the number determine its value? They may not be able to state this, but what they do will reveal whether they appreciate the importance of the position of the digits: they should be able to identify the hundreds position, the tens position and the ones position and realise that, for example, two in the tens position signifies more than two in the units position. Encourage the children to look at the position of the digits within the number. Which digit in the number has the greatest value? Which has the least?

Ask the children to organise the lists of numbers according to value, beginning with the largest number. Ask them to identify which of the numbers are odd and which are even

and see whether they can explain how they know. Do the children understand the importance of the last digit? Note whether individuals have attained the skills and understanding necessary to complete these tasks successfully. Use the recording grid to note the evidence and add comments as necessary. You might want to note down whether the child concentrated well, understood your instructions, was motivated, and so on.

Reference to photocopiable sheets

Photocopiable page 100 comprises a set of number cards.

FRACTIONS

Recognition that a set of objects can be divided into equal parts; recognition and use of the language of fractions, for example, a half and a quarter.
†† *Small group of up to three children.*
🕐 *10–15 minutes.*

Key background information

This task can be undertaken with up to three children. You will be assessing each child individually. The demands of the task are in keeping with the fraction requirements for Level 2, '... identify and use halves and quarters such as ... a quarter of eight objects'. The children will need to be given the chance to demonstrate their understanding by using the concrete materials and by explaining to you what they have done. The opportunity to talk and discuss with you is crucial. It is

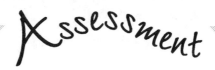
important to note that the inability to put down in writing or in symbols what they did may not signify lack of understanding of the concept being assessed, i.e. the ability to apply the language of fractions and to recognise that a set can be divided into equal parts.

Resources needed
12 counters for each child, paper and writing materials.

What to do
Distribute 12 counters to each child. Ask them to check if the counters could be shared equally between 2 people.

Observe the strategies they apply to do this problem and the language they use to explain what they did. Did they confidently and correctly divide the cubes into two equal groups of 6? Ask them to say what they did or how they knew. How many are in each group? Is there an equal number in each? Did they use the word 'half'?

Ask them to consider ways of recording what they have done. Examples might be 6 and 6, 6 + 6, 1/2 of 12 and 1/2 of 12. They may suggest 12 ÷ 2 = 6 (if they have been made aware of the division symbol, ÷). Allow them to suggest ideas. Next ask if they think they could divide the counters into four equal groups. Observe what they do. On the basis of this, do they know what 'equal' means? Again ask them questions to assess their understanding, e.g. Have you more or less in each group now than before? Are the groups equal? How do you know? Note the use of 'a quarter' or 'half of a half'. Once again, ask them to consider ways of recording what they have done. Examples might be: 3 + 3 + 3 +3, 1/4 of 12 is 3, 12 ÷ 4 = 3.

They ask them to write down all the ways they know of dividing 12 into equal shares, e.g. 12 ÷ 2, 12 ÷ 3, 12 ÷ 4, 12 ÷ 6. They could do this using pictures or symbols as follows:

or

4 + 4 + 4; 2 + 2 +2 + 2; 6 + 6;
1 + 1 + 1 + 1 + 1 + 1 + 1 + 1 + 1 + 1 + 1 + 1

or

12 ÷ 3 = 4; 12 ÷ 4 = 3; 12 ÷ 6 = 2; 12 ÷ 2 = 6

or

1/2 of 12 is 6; 1/3 of 12 is 4; 1/4 of 12 = 3;
1/6 of 12 = 2

Note the use of appropriate mathematical language as they work: shared, divided into equal shares, a half, a quarter, one-sixth and so on.

The written work they produce together with the responses they make to your questions provide evidence of their understanding. Key questions you need to be able to answer about the performance of each child are:

▲ Did the child succeed in arranging the counters into equal groups?

▲ Did she realise each group contained the same number of counters?

▲ Was she able to record this verbally and explain to you what she did?

▲ Did she use the language of fractions correctly and confidently, e.g. half, a quarter?

▲ Did she record some of the outcomes accurately in writing?

NUMBER PATTERNS

Recognition of pattern in numbers; building up number patterns; recognition of and being able to use patterns in addition and subtraction calculations; recognition of and being able to use patterns in multiplication and division calculations.

✸✸ *Small group of up to four children.*

🕐 *20–25 minutes.*

Key background information
This assessment task is designed to provide summative information on children's ability to recognise sequences of numbers and to use pattern to obtain number facts. It is in keeping with the demands of Level 2. The evidence on performance will be based on the children's responses to questions, their written work and on the arrangements of the counters.

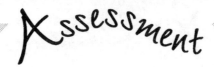
Preparation

Photocopy page101 to 105 and cut out the numbers. Photocopy page 125 (100 square). Arrange for children to work as a small group.

Resources needed

Photocopiable page101 to 105, photocopiable page 125 (100 square), collection of cubes or counters.

What to do

Distribute a collection of cubes or counters to each child in the group. Ask them to select 10 cubes or counters and make a pattern from them. Ask them to describe their patterns to you.

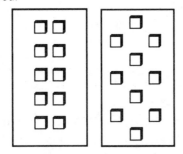

Ask them to record the pattern on paper using addition, for example:

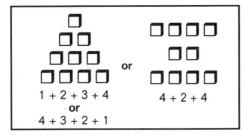

Let the children make patterns with other numbers of counters. Ask them if they can find shapes in their patterns, e.g. square numbers.

Distribute a set of number cards (from photocopiable sheets 101 to 105) to each child. Ask the children to think of two numbers that add up to make, for example, 10. (Allow the use of counters to assist them.) What other two numbers can they find?

Watch to see if they use a systematic pattern to find all the variations e.g. 1 + 4, 2 + 8, 3 + 7, 4 + 6, 5 + 5, 4 + 6 etc.

Ask them to look and see if there is a special order to their sums. If there is not, can they record their sums so that they are in a special order.

Ask them to describe what they have done and observe the use of terms such as even, odd, increasing, decreasing. The children can then look at three numbers that add up to 10. Examples might be 1 + 2 + 7, 1 + 3 + 6, 1 + 4 + 5, etc.

Then ask them to find different ways of subtracting two numbers to get, say, 6. (Allow the use of counters to assist them.) Once again, ask them to say what they have done. Do they notice and use the patterns in the numbers? Can they see how efficient it is to adopt a systematic approach, i.e. following a pattern rather than a random approach?

Distribute a 100 square grid. Ask the children to make up their own patterns using multiples of say, three. Ask them to find some multiplication and division facts from the pattern. Observe how they work and discuss the results with them. For example, in completing the grid do they quickly identify and use the pattern and predict what to shade next? Ask them to observe the completed table closely and tell you at least two things they notice about the pattern. For example, on the basis of the 100 grid in the illustration (shading multiples of three) the following conclusions might be drawn:

▲ There are 33 threes in 99

▲ 3 × 3 = 9

▲ The multiples of 9 form a pattern 9, 18, 27 etc.

▲ Every second number shaded is an even number.

Key questions you need to be able to answer about the performance of each child are:

▲ Did the child make and describe a pattern using the concrete materials?

▲ Did he accurately record the pattern on paper, using numbers to describe it?

▲ Did he use a systematic pattern to make 10 from pairs of numbers?

▲ Did he recognise the pattern?

▲ Did he describe the patterns using appropriate language e.g. add, even, increasing, decreasing?

▲ Did he successfully build up a pattern on a 100 square.

▲ Did he use the sequence or pattern to predict the next number?

▲ Did he make up sums based on the completed pattern?

1	2	3	4	5	6	7	8	9	10
11	12	13	14	15	16	17	18	19	20
21	22	23	24	25	26	27	28	29	30
31	32	33	34	35	36	37	38	39	40
41	42	43	44	45	46	47	48	49	50
51	52	53	54	55	56	57	58	59	60
61	62	63	64	65	66	67	68	69	70
71	72	73	74	75	76	77	78	79	80
81	82	83	84	85	86	87	88	89	90
91	92	93	94	95	96	97	98	99	100

Reference to photocopiable sheets

Photocopiable pages 101 to 105 comprises number cards and photocopiable page 125 provides a 100 square.

◆ OPERATIONS

Applying operations; division as the inverse of multiplication; division as sharing; problem solving.

†† *Individuals or pairs.*

🕐 *10–15 minutes.*

Preparation
Arrange for the children to work individually or in pairs.

Resources needed
Egg boxes or other similar container, collection of cubes or counters.

What to do
Place some counters in the egg box as follows:

Challenge the children to write a multiplication equation and a division equation to show what you have done, for example:

$3 \times 4 = 12$	$4 \times 3 = 12$
$12 \div 3 = 4$	$12 \div 4 = 3$

Ask the children to change the number of counters in the egg box and to make up more equations. Observe their ability to do this.

◆ SHOPPING

Applying the four operations; using a calculator; knowing which operations to apply; handling coins (money) effectively; checking results using a calculator; estimating; problem solving.

†† *Two to four children.*

🕐 *10 to 20 minutes.*

Key background information
This task demands the application of operations in a shopping situation. It assesses pupils' ability to use calculator methods and demonstrates whether they have begun to develop mental strategies for adding and subtracting numbers with two digits. (It also assesses the pupils' ability to use decimal notation.) These demands are in line with the requirements for Level 3.

Preparation
Prepare copies of photocopiable page 146 (class café price list) for each pair of children.

Resources needed
Photocopiable page 146 (class café price list), collection of coins of different value, calculator.

What to do
Ask the children to work in pairs. Give one copy of the class café price list from photocopiable page 146 to one member of each pair. Give the other child a pound coin and ask him to decide what drink he would like to buy. The other child must then work out the correct change to be given from one pound.

Observe the strategies used. For example, is the child able to count on? Let the children take it in turns to give change. Do they realise that £1 is made up of 100p? Are they able to subtract 2-digit numbers, e.g. 40p from £1? Do they count on in jumps of 10, i.e. 50, 60, 70, 80, 90 and £1? Can they mix the jumps, for example 78p from £1; 80p, 90p and £1? Furthermore, can they handle coins effectively? Do they recognise, for example, that a 20 pence coin is more convenient than two 10 pence coins?

Next ask one child to select two or three things on the list which they could buy for under one pound. The other child should be asked to check the total price of all the choices by using a calculator. Are they able to add two 2-digit numbers? Are they able to estimate sensibly? Are they able to use a calculator to check estimates? Check their ability to estimate the answer. Allow both children to do this a couple of times.

Next go on to situations which would involve multiplication as a quick way of adding. For example, pose the problem that three people want to buy a milk shake. How would you quickly calculate the cost of this? What if four people wanted

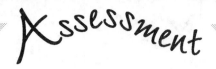
to buy chips? Ask them to estimate the cost first and then to check their estimates using the calculator to work it out. Do they know which operation to apply? What suggestions do they offer? Do they mention 'multiply'? Note whether they can use the calculator confidently and reliably. Did they offer reasonable estimates before checking with the calculator?

Ask them to estimate how many pastries, packets of crisps and so on they could buy for one pound. Ask them how to work out and check the answer. What suggestions do they offer? Do they mention 'divide'? For example, do they mention dividing 100p by 14?

Allow children lots of opportunities to demonstrate what they know and can do in these contexts.

Reference to photocopiable sheets

Photocopiable page 146 provides a price list.

DATA HANDLING

Data interpretation; representing information in a variety of ways; interpreting information presented in a variety of ways.

†† *Groups of three or four or more, working individually.*

🕐 *20–30 minutes.*

Key background information

This task demands that pupils interpret information presented in simple tables, that they construct graphs using a simple scale and that they interpret and summarise their graphs. The demands are in line with Level 3.

Preparation

Prepare a tally table of information for each child as follows:

The number of left-handed children in Poppletown schools	
Castle School	
Victoria School	
Acorn School	
Tower School	
Park School	

Arrange to observe and talk with individual children as they work.

Resources needed

A tally table, writing materials, squared paper for drawing graph.

What to do

Distribute a tally table to each child. Spend a few minutes with the group discussing what it is. Ask them to say, for example, how they think the information was collected. Ask them to suggest why they think the data might have been collected.

Next ask them to work individually and think about how they might construct a block graph of this information. Ask them to think about using a scale and to decide what scale might be appropriate. Tell them you will go around to each one to see how they are doing and to discuss their scales. Ask them to put as much information as they think is needed on the graph.

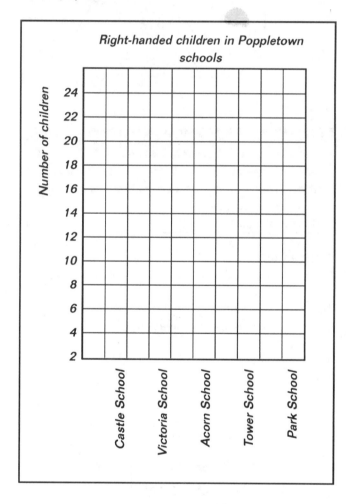

As they work, check each child's responses to your request. Can they both read and interpret the tally table? Do they know what a block graph is? How do they decide what scale to use? Do they check the numbers in the largest category or in the school? Can they see the purposes of the scale? Do they label the block graph appropriately with title, labels on horizontal and vertical axes, numbers in the boxes/ spaces, not on lines etc? Can they interpret the graph by writing three or four summary statements about it, for example, Tower School has the most left-handed children; Victoria School has the least; five schools took part in the survey, etc?

Photocopiables

The pages in this section can be photocopied for use in the classroom or school which has purchased this book, and do not need to be declared in any return in respect of any photocopying licence.

They comprise a varied selection of both pupil and teacher resources, including pupil worksheets, resource material and record sheets to be completed by the teacher or children. Most of the photocopiable pages are related to individual activities in the book; the name of the activity is indicated at the top of the sheet, together with a page reference indicating where the lesson plan for that activity can be found.

Individual pages are discussed in detail within each lesson plan, accompanied by ideas for adaptation where appropriate – of course, each sheet can be adapted to suit your own needs and those of your class. Sheets can also be coloured, laminated, mounted on to card, enlarged and so on where appropriate.

Pupil worksheets and record sheets have spaces provided for children's names and for noting the date on which each sheet was used. This means that, if so required, they can be included easily within any pupil assessment portfolio.

Match the animals, see page 14

Match the animals cards

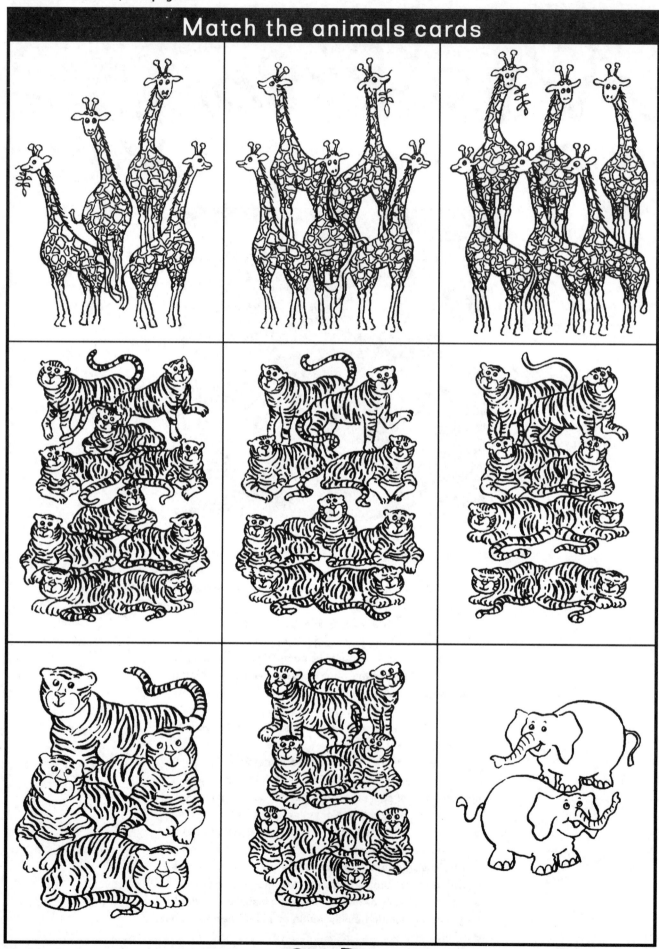

NUMBER

Match the animals, see page 14

Match the animals cards

Building 2-digit numbers, see page 16

Building 2-digit number cards

0	1	2
3	4	5
6	7	8
	9	

Largest number wins, see page 18

Largest number wins number cards

0	1	2	3
4	5	6	7
8	9	10	11
12	13	14	15
16	17	18	19

Largest number wins, see page 18

Largest number wins number cards

20	21	22	23
24	25	26	27
28	29	30	31
32	33	34	35
36	37	38	39

Largest number wins, see page 18

Largest number wins number cards

40	41	42	43
44	45	46	47
48	49	50	51
52	53	54	55
56	57	58	59

Largest number wins, see page 18

Largest number wins number cards

60	61	62	63
64	65	66	67
68	69	70	71
72	73	74	75
76	77	78	79

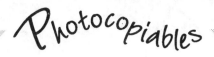

Photocopiables

Largest number wins, see page 18

Largest number wins number cards

80	81	82	83
84	85	86	87
88	89	90	91
92	93	94	95
96	97	98	99

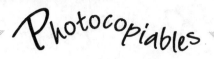

Largest number wins, see page 18

Largest number wins recording sheet

Name _____   Date _____

	My number	Number of counters	Our numbers ending with the largest			
1						
2						
3						
4						
5						
6						
7						
8						
9						
10						

Race to £1, see page 19

Board game for Race to £1

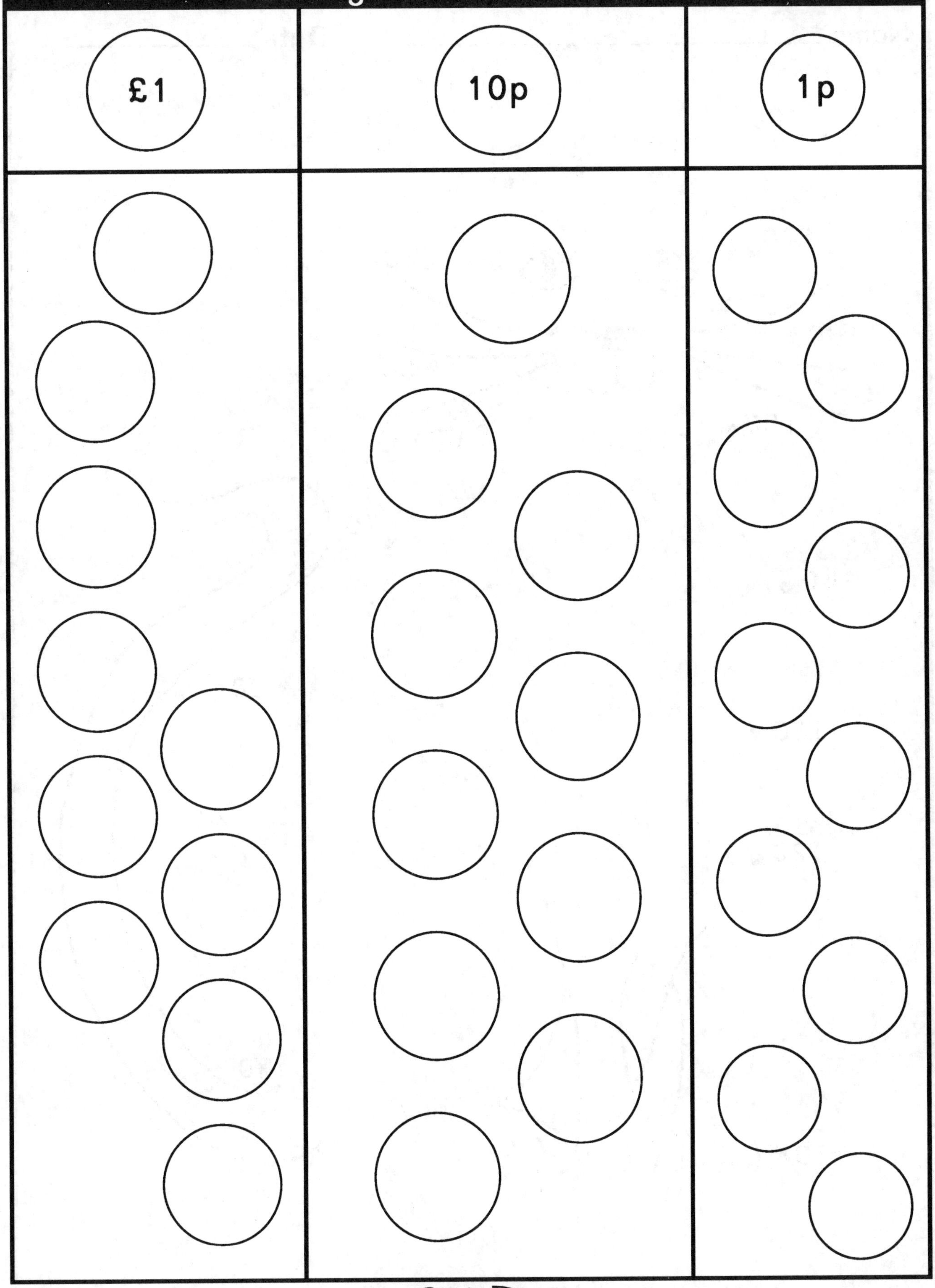

£1	10p	1p

NUMBER

Dotty numbers, see page 20

Dot-to-dot

Name _____   Date _____

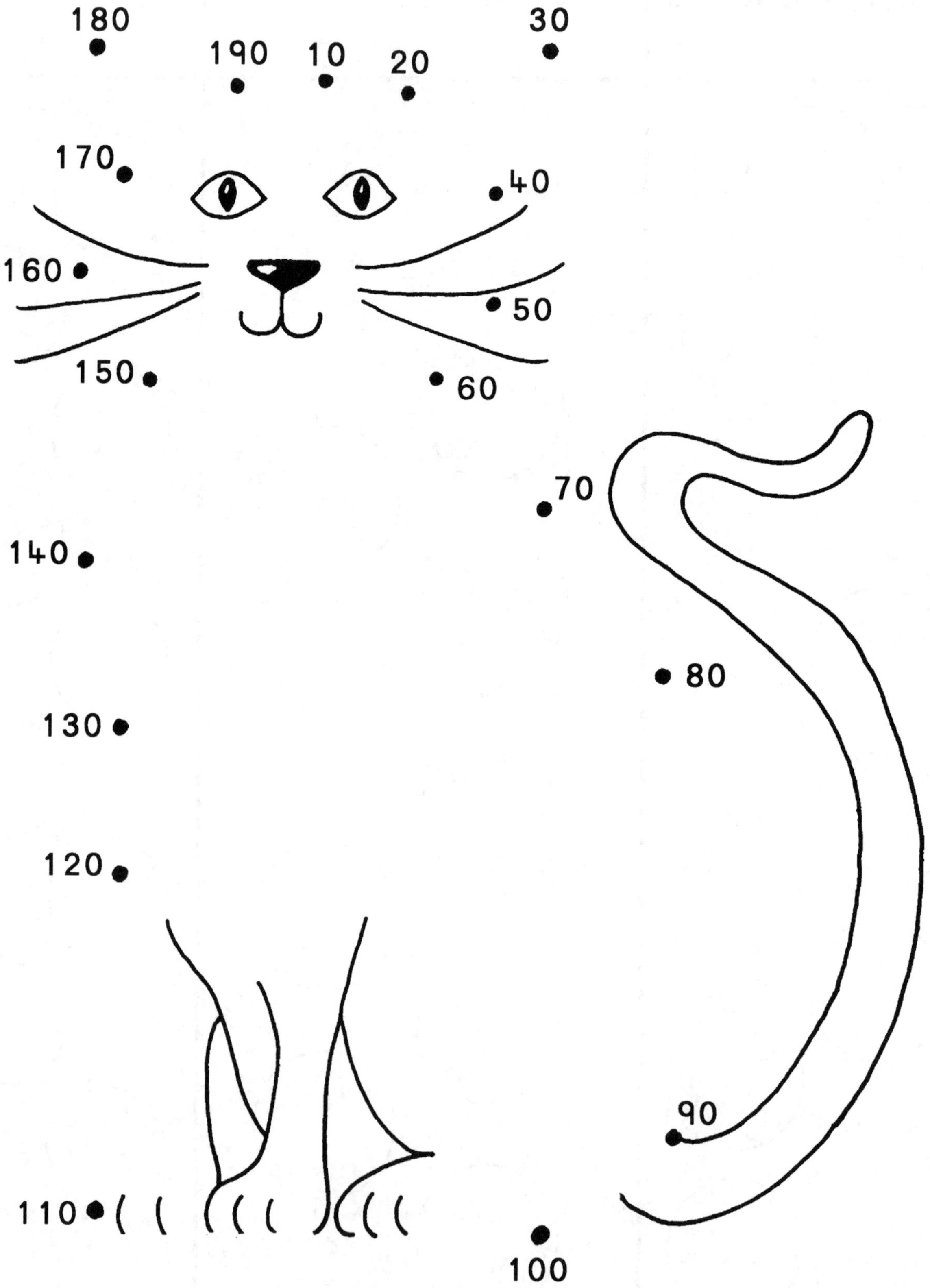

180
190   10   20
30
170
40
160
50
150
60
70
140
80
130
120
110
100
90

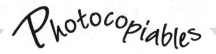

Dotty numbers, see page 20

Dot-to-dot

Name _____   Date _____

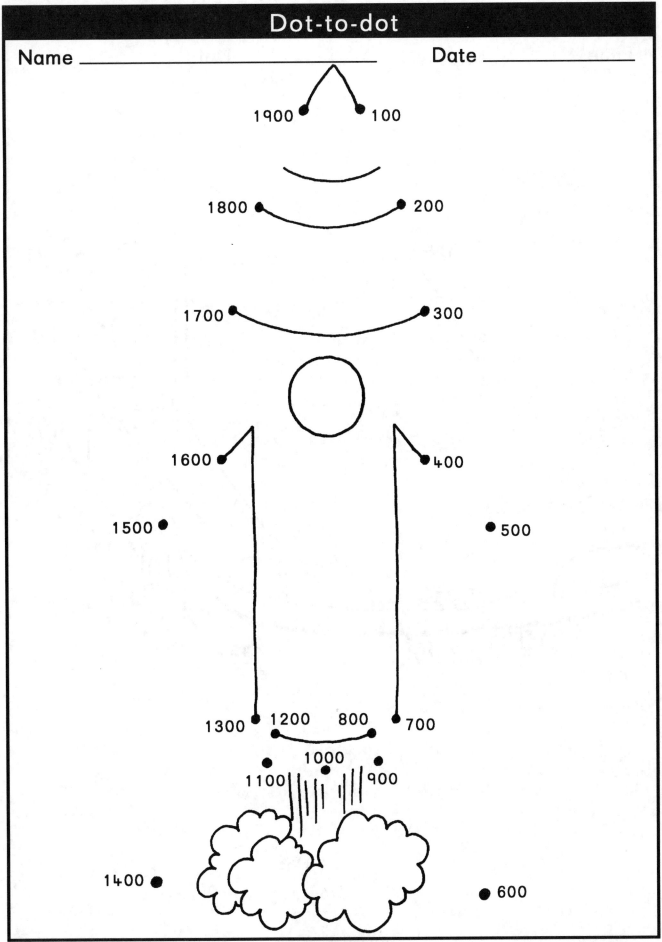

NUMBER

Dotty numbers, see page 20

Dot-to-dot

Name _____   Date _____

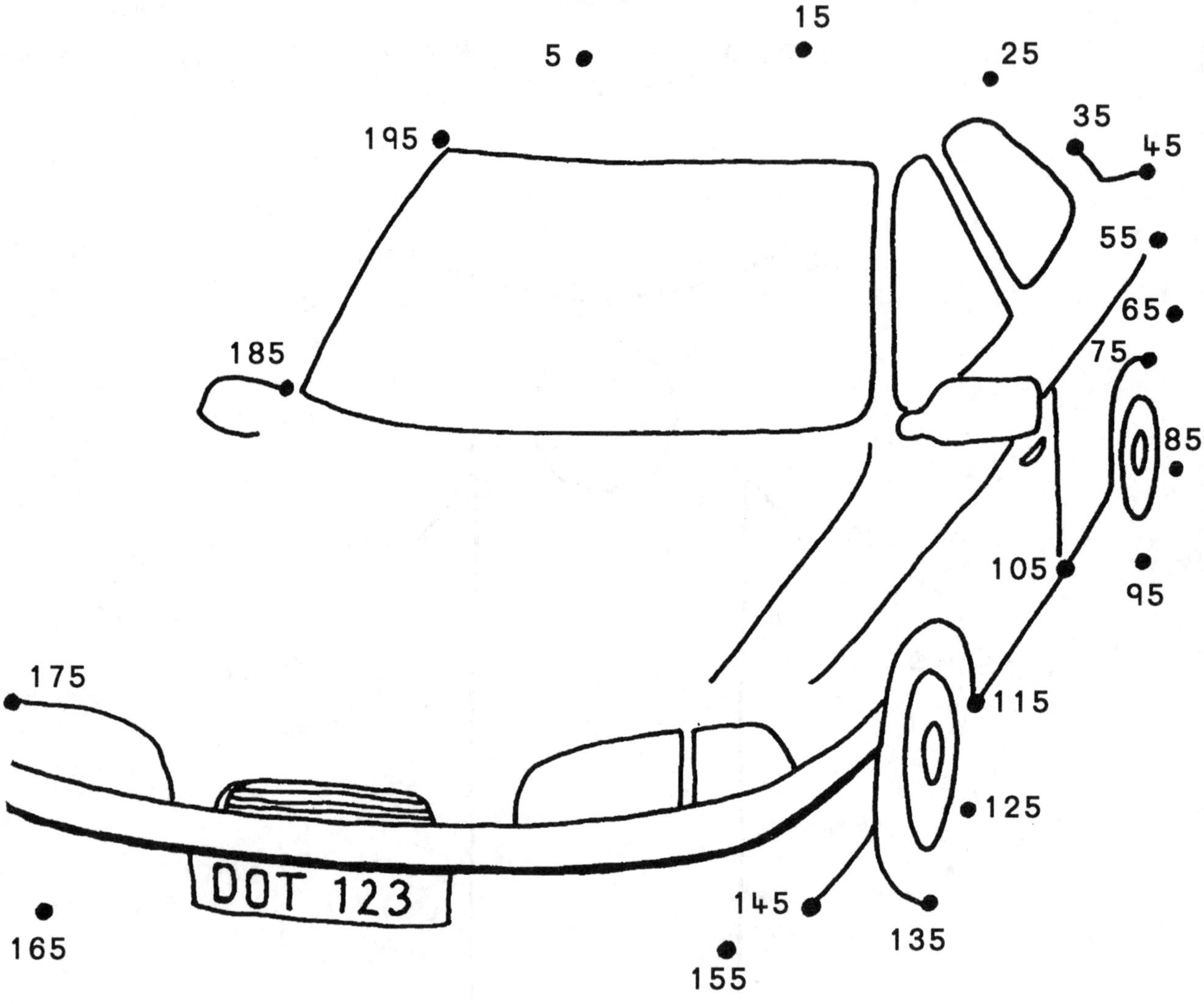

15

5

25

35

45

195

55

65

75

185

85

105

95

175

115

125

145

135

165

155

DOT 123

Dotty numbers, see page 20

Dot-to-dot

Name _____ Date _____

Money money money, see page 23

Money money money

50p

30p

£3.20

98p

8p

£1.05

£1.50

£2.50

£3.00

45p

£5

5p

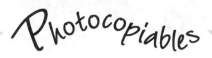
Price cards

£0.08	£0.45	£0.50	£3.00
£5.00	£3.20	£0.98	£0.05
£1.50	£1.05	£2.50	£0.30
8p	45p	50p	300p
500p	320p	98p	5p
150p	105p	250p	30p

Money money money, see page 23

Price tags

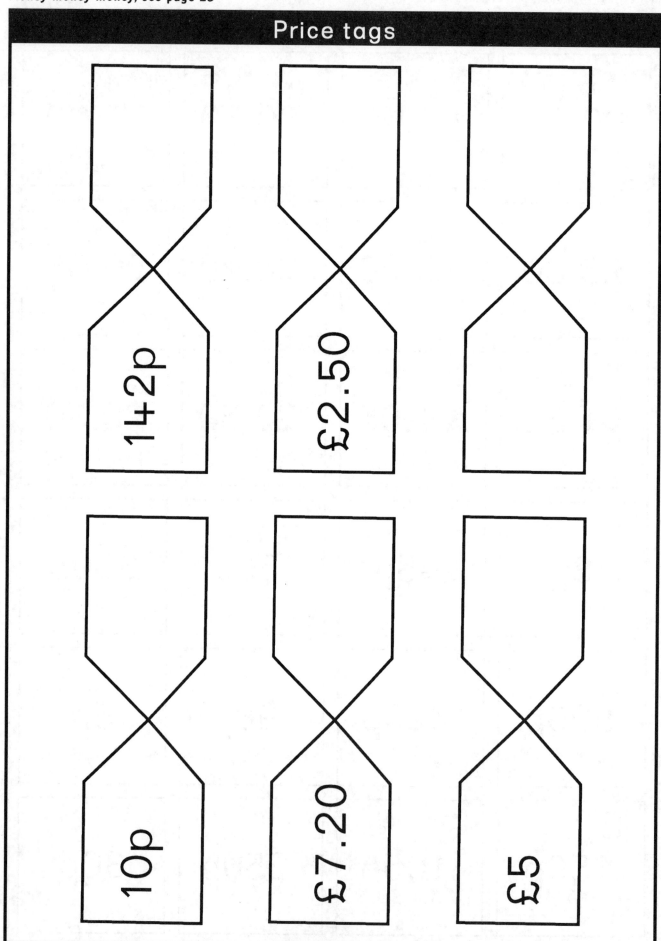

142p

£2.50

10p

£7.20

£5

NUMBER

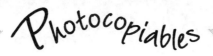

Multiply by 10 and 100, see page 24

Multiply by 10 and 100 recording sheet

Name _____   Date _____

Dice number	Multiply by 1	Multiply by 10	Multiply by 100
3	3	30	300

Matching halves, see page 27

Matching halves

Sharing between three, see page 29

Sharing biscuits

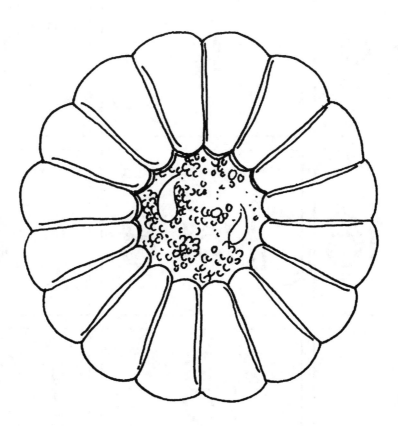

Finding more fractions, see page 31

Fraction cards

$\frac{1}{2}$ of 8	4	4
$\frac{1}{4}$ of 16	$\frac{1}{4}$ of 8	8
8	2	$\frac{1}{2}$ of 16
$\frac{1}{4}$ of 32	=	=
=	=	=

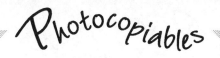

Finding more fractions, see page 31

Finding more fractions cards

one half

one half

one quarter

one quarter

one quarter

one quarter

one sixth

one sixth

one sixth

one sixth

one sixth

one sixth

one eighth

one eighth

one eighth

one eighth

one eighth

one eighth

one eighth

one eighth

Dress the teddy, see page 35

Dress the teddy

Number arrays, see page 37

Number cards

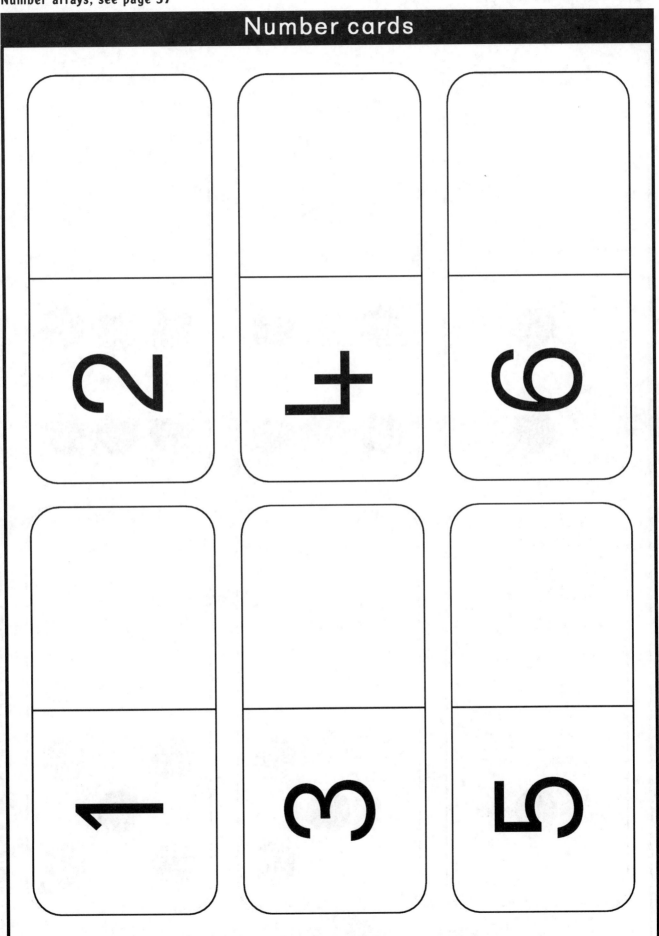

Number arrays, see page 37

Dot cards

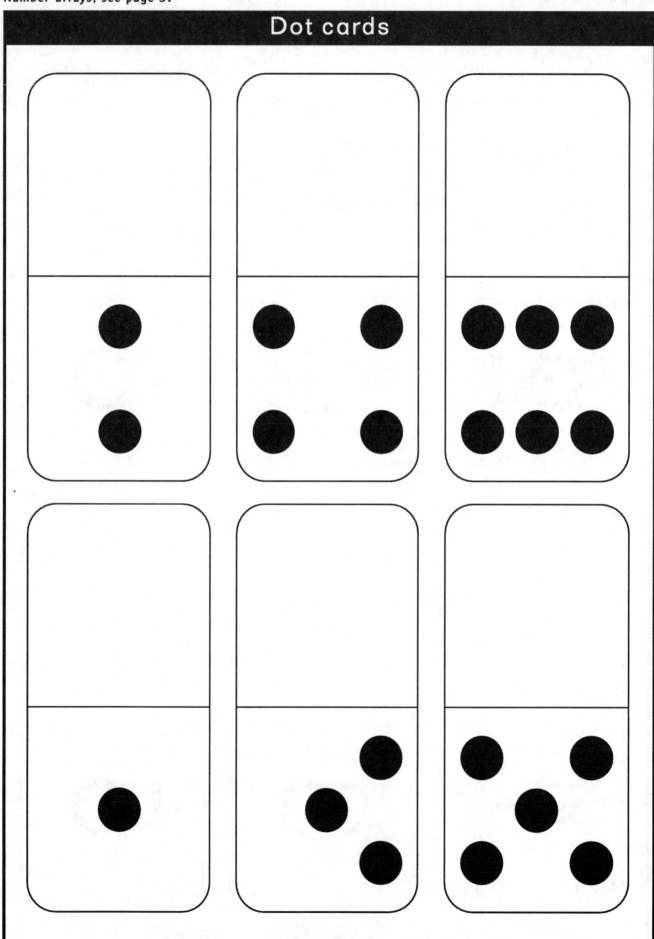

Subtraction patterns, see page 39

Subtraction patterns

Name _____   Date _____

$$\boxed{} - \boxed{} = 2 \qquad \boxed{} - \boxed{} = 2$$

$$\boxed{} - \boxed{} = 2 \qquad \boxed{} - \boxed{} = 2$$

$$\boxed{} - \boxed{} = 2 \qquad \boxed{} - \boxed{} = 2$$

$$\boxed{} - \boxed{} = 2 \qquad \boxed{} - \boxed{} = 2$$

$$\boxed{} - \boxed{} = 2 \qquad \boxed{} - \boxed{} = 2$$

$$\boxed{} - \boxed{} = 2 \qquad \boxed{} - \boxed{} = 2$$

$$\boxed{} - \boxed{} = 2 \qquad \boxed{} - \boxed{} = 2$$

$$\boxed{} - \boxed{} = 2 \qquad \boxed{} - \boxed{} = 2$$

Number grids, see page 40

Number grids

Name _____ Date _____

Number grids, see page 40

10 x 10 number grid

Number grids, see page 40

25-square recording sheet

Name _____   Date _____

Write the number patterns you have found using the 25 square.

Counting in   2   s

Counting in   5   s

Counting in   10   s

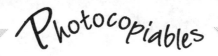

Number grids, see page 40

100-square recording sheet

Name _____   Date _____

Write the number patterns you have found using the 100 square.

Counting in | 2 | s

Counting in | 5 | s

Counting in | 10 | s

Counting in | | s

Counting in | | s

Number quiz, see page 44

2s number quiz cards				
2 x 4	2 x 8	4	12	20
2 x 3	2 x 7	2	10	18
2 x 2	2 x 6	2 x 10	8	16
2 x 1	2 x 5	2 x 9	6	14

Number quiz, see page 44

5s number quiz cards

5 x 4	5 x 8	10	30	50
5 x 3	5 x 7	5	25	45
5 x 2	5 x 6	5 x 10	20	40
5 x 1	5 x 5	5 x 9	15	35

Number quiz, see page 44

10s number quiz cards

10 x 4	10 x 8	20	60	100
10 x 3	10 x 7	10	50	90
10 x 2	10 x 6	10 x 10	40	80
10 x 1	10 x 5	10 x 9	30	70

Number chains (1) and (2), see pages 46 and 47

Number chains

Name _____ Date _____

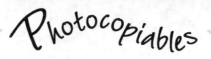

Odd and even, see page 50

Odd and even recording sheet

Name _____   Date _____

_____
won this
game

_____
won this
game

_____
won this
game

_____
won this
game

_____
won this
game

_____
won this
game

_____
won this
game

_____
won this
game

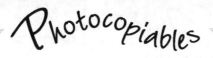

Square numbers, see page 51

Square numbers recording sheet

Name _____   Date _____

I have discovered these square numbers.

Number	Pattern

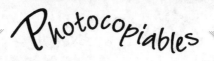

Rectangular numbers, see page 52

Rectangular numbers recording sheet

Name _____   Date _____

I have discovered these rectangular numbers.

Number	Pattern

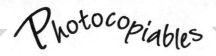

Negative numbers, see page 54

Negative numbers recording sheet

Name _____   Date _____

Use your calculator and record your results below.

7	−	9	=	
3	−	4	=	
	−		=	
	−		=	
	−		=	
	−		=	
	−		=	
	−		=	

Curriculum Bank
135

The toy shop, see page 56

The toy shop window

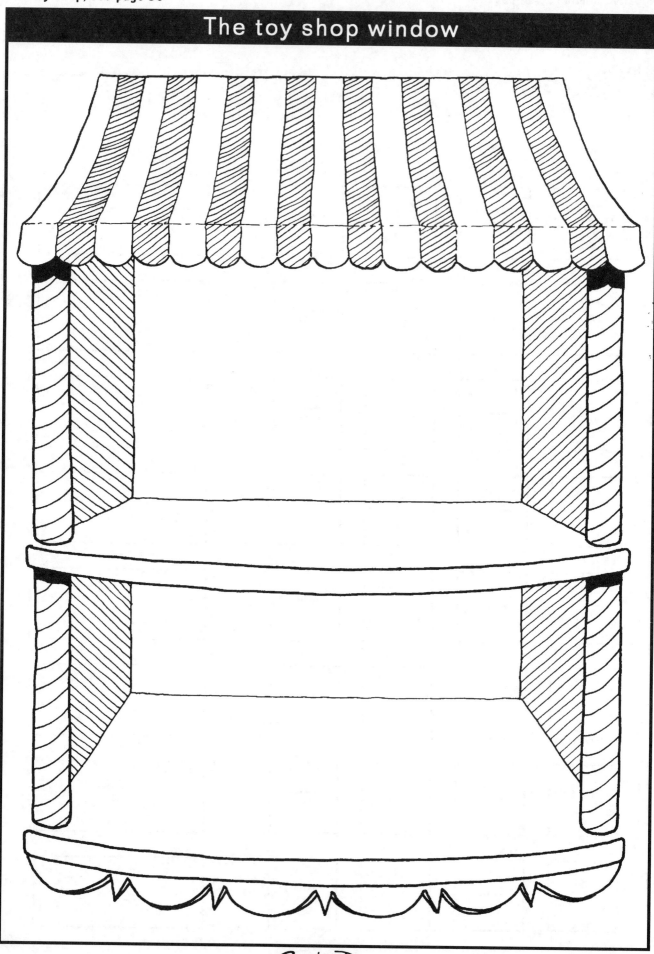

NUMBER

Photocopiables

The toy shop, see page 56

Toy cards

Change from 20 pence, see page 57

Change from 20p cards

11p	12p	13p	15p
16p	19p	18p	20p
2p	6p	3p	5p
7p	8p	9p	10p

Change from £1, see page 59

Change from £1 cards

45p	25p	18p	17p
22p	34p	12p	29p
67p	88p	98p	55p
79p	85p	70p	51p

A board game, see page 63

Race track game

A board game, see page 63

Board game question cards

$\begin{array}{r} 2 \\ 3 \\ + 6 \\ \hline \end{array}$	What is the number before 65 ?	$\begin{array}{r} 33 \\ + 3 \\ \hline \end{array}$	What is the number before 97 ?
$\begin{array}{r} 11p \\ + \\ 5p \end{array}$	The number after 0 is ?	$2p + \square = 9p$	What is the difference between 12 and 8 ?
$\begin{array}{r} 13 \\ - 5 \\ \hline \end{array}$	$\begin{array}{r} 8 \\ + 6 \\ \hline \end{array}$	$\begin{array}{r} 8 \\ + \square \\ \hline 17 \end{array}$	$\frac{1}{2}$ of 2

A board game, see page 63

Board game question cards

$\frac{1}{2}$ of 22	How much change from £1?	5p+2p+3p+1p	18 fish and 2 fish. How many altogether?
How much altogether?	What is the difference between 20 and 10?	50 − 15	19 + 8
What number is missing? 28, 27, 26, ☐, 24	How much money?	30p − ☐ = 20p	6 + 6 = 5 + ☐

A board game, see page 63

Board game question cards

Ann has 10p. John has no money. Sarah has 10p. How much have they altogether?	How many is 4 sets of 10? ☐	Share 9 sweets among Bob, May and Jim. How many each?	3 × ☐ = 15
How many groups of 5 are there?	How many is 3 sets of 4? ☐	20 ÷ 4 = ☐	9 × 5 = ☐
Amit has no money. Renzo gave half of his £18 to Amit. How much has Amit now?	☐ × 5 = 35	8 boys each buy a 10p cake. How much money do they spend altogether?	9 + ☐ = 14

A board game, see page 63

Board game question cards

$18 \div 3 =$ ▢

Jim was born in 1990

What age is he?

Ann had 80p. She lost 10p. Then her mum gave her 20p.

How much has Ann now?

$99 + 2 =$ ▢

Share 50p between Renzo and Amit. Give Amit 10p more than Renzo. How much do they each have?

$\begin{array}{r} 19 \\ + 5 \\ + 5 \\ \hline \end{array}$

▢ $\times 4 = 16$

▢ $4 + 2 \times 5 =$

The pen costs 85p. How much change would there be from £1? ▢

The pencils cost 10p. I have £1.

Can I buy 5?

$3 + 2 + 9 + 0 =$ ▢

$\begin{array}{r} 18 \\ - 6 \\ \hline \end{array}$

The class shop, see page 64

Price tags

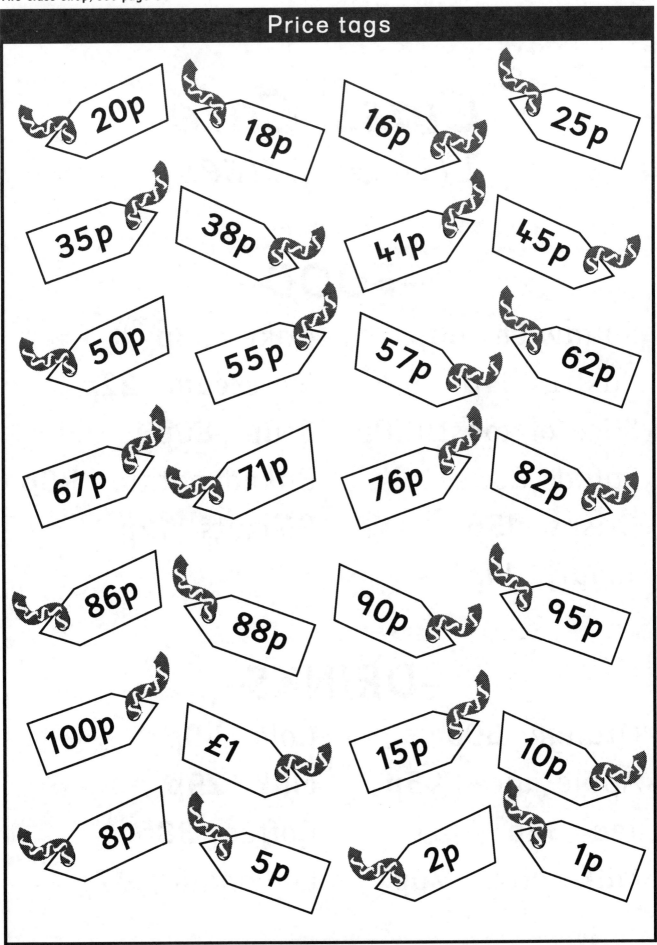

20p 18p 16p 25p

35p 38p 41p 45p

50p 55p 57p 62p

67p 71p 76p 82p

86p 88p 90p 95p

100p £1 15p 10p

8p 5p 2p 1p

Class café, see page 65

Class café menu

Class Café
List of prices

–FOOD–

Sandwich **60p**	Cake **33p**
Pastry **14p**	Ice cream **22p**
Slice of toast **10p**	Soup **80p**
Salad **83p**	Baked potato **90p**
Crisps **15p**	Biscuits **12p**
Yogurt **19p**	

–DRINKS–

Orange **30p**	Cola **40p**
Apple juice **45p**	Milk **29p**
Tea **32p**	Coffee **38p**
Milk shake **70p**	Lemonade **37p**

Photocopiables

Multiplication as repeated addition, see page 66

Multiplication as repeated addition

Name _____ Date _____

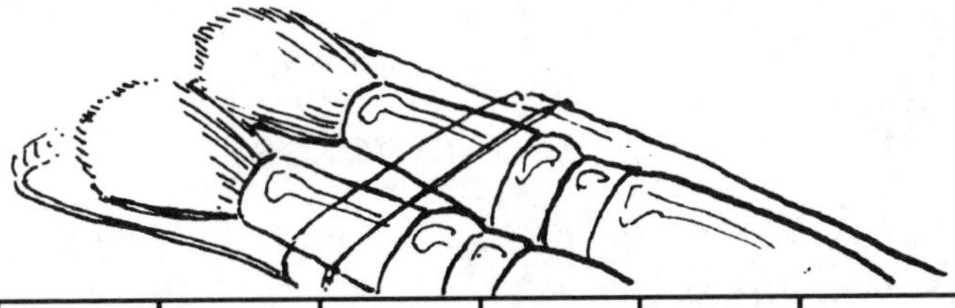

packet	1	2	3	4	5	6	7	8	9	10
paint brushes										

packet	1	2	3	4	5	6	7	8	9	10
pens										

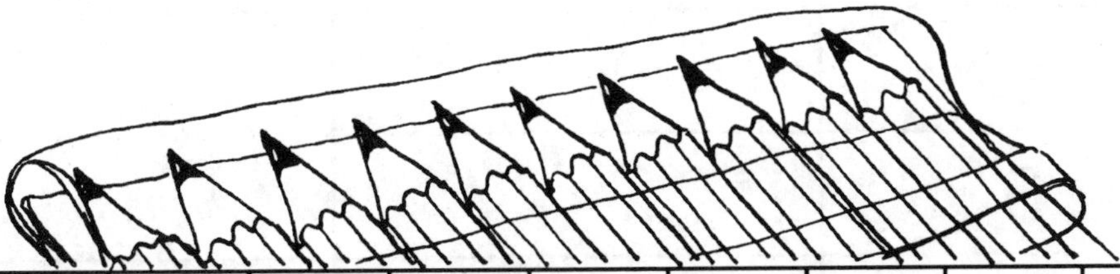

packet	1	2	3	4	5	6	7	8	9	10
pencils										

Curriculum Bank
147

NUMBER

Division as sharing, see page 68

Boxing candles

Name _____ Date _____

At the factory, candles are packed in boxes,
10 candles go in each box.
How many candles will fill 5 boxes?
How many boxes can be filled if you have 72 candles?
Are any candles left over?

Fill in the table

Number of candles	Number of boxes that can be filles	How many candles left over?
72		
43		
19		
67		
104		
38		
50		
6		
85		

Number of boxes that can be filled
How many candles left over
How many candles would exactly fill

4 boxes? ☐   7 boxes? ☐   11 boxes? ☐

Division as sharing, see page 68

Division as sharing workcards

Get 15 cubes.

Make a tower of 5.

How many
towers of 5
can you make?

Get 10 2p coins.

An ice pop costs 4p.

How many
can you buy?

How many eggs are
there?

How many groups of 2
can you make?

How many flowers are
there?

How many groups of 3
can you make?

How many groups of
four are there?

Get 20 bricks.

Build some walls of 5
bricks.

How many walls
can you build?

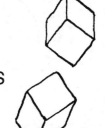

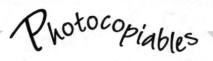

Counting on and adding on, see page 70

Counting on and adding on board game

START

1 2 3 4 5 6 7 8 9 10 11 12

22 21 20 19 18 17 16 15 14 13

23

24

25

26 27 28 29 30 31 32 33 34 35 36 37

38

39

40

50 49 48 47 46 45 44 43 42 41

51

52

53 54 55 56 57 58 59 60 61 62 63

64

65

66

75 74 73 72 71 70 69 68 67

76

77 78 79 80 81 82 83 84 85 86

Ten seconds only, see page 72

Ten seconds only sum cards

2 x 2	2 x 3	4 x 2
5 x 2	2 x 6	7 x 2
8 x 2	2 x 9	10 x 2
1 x 2	0 x 5	5 x 1
5 x 2	3 x 5	4 x 5
5 x 5	5 x 6	7 x 5
8 x 5	9 x 5	10 x 5

Ten seconds only, see page 72

Ten seconds only sum and number cards

10 x 2	3 x 10	4 x 10
5 x 10	6 x 10	10 x 7
8 x 10	10 x 9	10 x 10
1 x 10	4	6
8	10	12
14	16	18
20	2	0

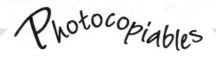
Ten seconds only number cards

5	10	15
20	25	30
35	40	45
50	20	30
40	50	60
70	80	90
100	21	13

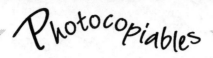
Number journeys recording sheet

Name _____ **Date** _____

Number journeys	My check

USING AND APPLYING MATHEMATICS

This section of the programme of study should be set in the context of the other sections. It is very important that the children are given opportunities to use and apply mathematics in practical activities, in real-life problems and within mathematics itself. Using and applying mathematics can only occur in relation to the knowledge and understanding of other aspects of the curriculum. It is an approach and not a body of knowledge in itself. Children should be given the opportunity to explain their thinking to support the development of their reasoning. Aspects of the using and applying approach are included within almost all the activities in this book. The table on pages 156 and 157shows where there may be opportunities for the teacher to incorporate using and applying mathematics into activities.

The programme of study for using and applying

mathematics is divided into three main sub-sections: making and monitoring decisions to solve problems; developing mathematical language and communication; and developing mathematical reasoning. Each sub-section is further sub-divided into three or four separate aspects.

The 'using and applying' aspects of the mathematics National Curriculum provide the context within which the content of the curriculum is taught and learned. There has to be a balance between those activities which develop knowledge, skills and understanding, and those which develop the ability to tackle practical problems. The processes involved in the 'using and applying' dimension enable pupils to make use of and communicate their mathematical knowledge; for many pupils this is the main point in learning mathematics.

The diagram below shows the context, content and process dimensions of mathematics teaching.

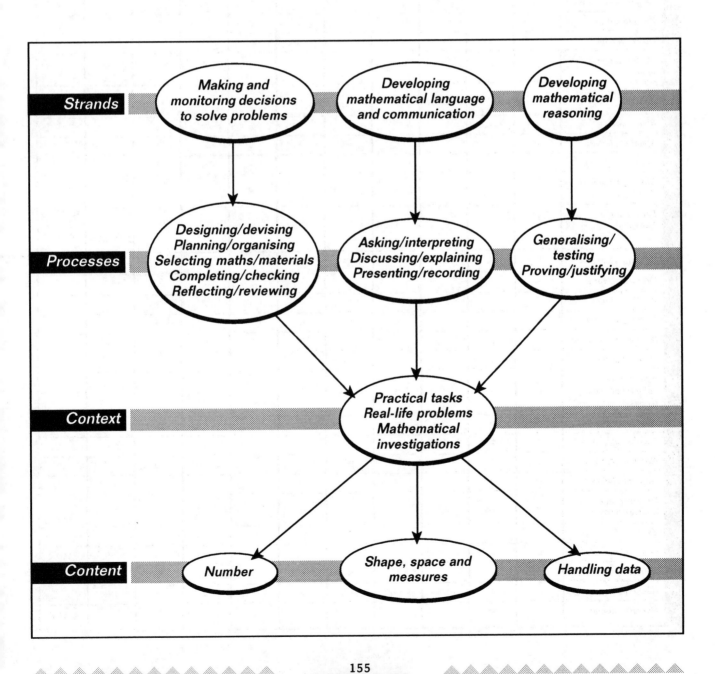

	ACTIVITIES	SOLVING PROBLEMS				COMMUNICATION				LOGICAL REASONING		
		Pupils select and use the appropriate mathematics.	Pupils select and use mathematical equipment and materials.	Pupils develop different mathematical approaches and look for ways to overcome difficulties.	Pupils organise and check their work.	Pupils understand the language of number properties of shapes and comparatives.	Pupils relate numerals and other mathematical symbols to a range of situations.	Pupils discuss their work, responding to and asking mathematical questions.	Pupils use a variety of forms of mathematical presentation.	Pupils ask questions including 'What would happen if...?' and 'Why?'	Pupils recognise simple patterns and relationships and make related predictions about them.	Pupils understand general statements and investigate whether particular cases match them.
		a	b	c	d	a	b	c	d	a	b	c
Number system and place value	Match the animals	●	●			●		●	●	●		
	Cuddly toys					●		●	●			
	Building 2-digit numbers	●	●		●	●		●	●			
	Largest number wins	●	●			●		●				
	Race to £1	●	●		●	●		●		●		●
	Dotty numbers	●	●	●	●	●	●	●	●	●	●	●
	Money, money, money	●	●			●		●	●	●		●
	Multiply by 10 and 100	●	●		●	●	●	●	●	●	●	
	Equal parts		●			●		●		●		●
	Matching halves	●	●		●	●	●	●				●
	Partitioning sets	●	●			●		●	●	●		
	Sharing between three	●	●	●	●	●	●	●	●			
	Finding more fractions	●	●		●	●	●	●	●	●		●
Number relationships	Spot the pattern					●		●	●	●		
	Dress the teddy	●				●		●	●	●		
	Number arrays					●		●	●	●		
	Building up numbers	●	●		●		●	●	●	●		
	Subtraction patterns	●	●			●		●	●	●		●
	Number grids	●	●		●	●	●	●	●	●	●	●
	Addition and subtraction board games	●	●		●			●	●			
	Number of the day	●	●	●	●	●	●	●	●	●		●
	Number quiz	●	●	●	●			●	●			
	Number chains 1	●	●			●	●	●	●	●		
	Number chains 2	●	●		●			●	●	●		
	Discover more number facts	●	●		●			●	●	●		
	Zero		●			●		●	●			
	Odd and even	●	●			●		●	●	●	●	●
	Square numbers	●	●			●	●	●	●	●		●
	Rectangular numbers	●	●		●	●		●	●	●		
	Negative numbers		●		●	●	●	●	●	●		●

ACTIVITIES	SOLVING PROBLEMS				COMMUNICATION				LOGICAL REASONING		
	Pupils select and use the appropriate mathematics.	Pupils select and use mathematical equipment and materials.	Pupils develop different mathematical approaches and look for ways to overcome difficulties.	Pupils organise and check their work.	Pupils understand the language of number properties of shapes and comparatives.	Pupils relate numerals and other mathematical symbols to a range of situations.	Pupils discuss their work, responding to and asking mathematical questions.	Pupils use a variety of forms of mathematical presentation.	Pupils ask questions including 'What would happen if...?' and 'Why?'	Pupils recognise simple patterns and relationships and make related predictions about them.	Pupils understand general statements and investigate whether particular cases match them.
	a	b	c	d	a	b	c	d	a	b	c

Calculations and problem solving

ACTIVITIES	a	b	c	d	a	b	c	d	a	b	c
The toy shop	●		●	●	●	●	●		●		
Change from 20 pence	●	●	●	●	●	●	●		●		
Change from £1	●	●	●	●	●	●	●		●		
Beginning multiplication	●	●		●	●	●	●	●	●		
Beginning division	●	●		●	●		●		●		
A board game	●			●		●	●				
The class shop	●		●	●			●	●			
Class café	●	●	●	●			●				
Multiplication as repeated addition		●	●	●	●	●	●	●			
Division as sharing	●	●		●			●	●			
Three dice addition	●	●	●	●	●	●	●		●		
Counting on and adding on	●			●			●				
How many cubes?	●		●	●			●				
Ten seconds only	●			●		●	●				
Check your journey	●			●	●	●	●	●			
Brothers and sisters	●			●	●		●		●	●	●
More adding and checking	●			●	●		●		●		

Handling data

ACTIVITIES	a	b	c	d	a	b	c	d	a	b	c
Sorting ourselves out	●	●			●		●	●	●		
Sorting using Carroll diagrams	●	●		●			●	●	●		
Tallying	●	●	●	●	●		●	●	●		
Recording using a two-way table	●			●			●	●	●		●
Block graphs	●			●	●		●	●	●	●	●
Using a scale	●			●	●		●	●	●	●	●

Assessment

ACTIVITIES	a	b	c	d	a	b	c	d	a	b	c
Count the animals	●	●		●	●	●	●		●		●
Three digit numbers	●			●	●	●	●		●		
Fractions	●			●	●	●	●	●	●		
Number patterns	●	●	●	●	●		●	●	●		●
Operations	●	●				●	●	●	●		
Shopping	●	●	●	●			●		●		
Data handling	●			●	●		●	●	●		●

INFORMATION TECHNOLOGY WITHIN MATHS

There is a vast array of software for use in mathematics and finding a way through it can be confusing and time-consuming. The following ideas may prove useful in evaluating software for use in mathematics.

What is the purpose of using the software?

Clearly this should be the central concern of the teacher. If the software is being used because it fulfils a particular need for a particular child or group of children then it could be valuable.

Can the content be matched to the child's age and ability?

Can you select options from a sensible choice which are matched to the needs of your children? Are they versatile enough to cover a wide range or are they targeted very precisely to a single user? If the sub-divisions in a number bond reinforcement program are too large, the resulting questions may either be too easy or too hard for the child.

Check that the reading level of the instructions within the software is suitable for the children using it. Graphical prompts can be more helpful than words, particularly for younger children. If there are instructions for the child, are they within the child's reading ability and can they return to the instructions if they need to?

Are the questions used in the program good ones? If they are chosen randomly, do the same ones keep re-appearing too frequently? Random selections can even throw up combinations that the programmer didn't envisage which can give rise to quite meaningless questions.

Can you select the speed at which questions are asked? If they change too quickly it may not give the child time to respond and may just frustrate the child rather than give useful practice.

Is the screen presentation well planned?

This can cover a number of different areas and include not only the sequence of the program but the way in which graphics or words are used on the screen. Large chunky letters may be difficult for children to read, especially if the screen is very cluttered. On the other hand, small letters may not be large enough for young children. Letter shapes may also be different from the style used in school.

Where children are asked to move an object around the screen, the speed of the cursor movement in relation to the use of keys or mouse is important. Too fast and the child will overshoot the targets and become frustrated with the task; too slow and children may become bored. Again, where this is a feature of the program, look for the ability to alter the speed of cursor or mouse movement.

Colours should provide a strong contrast where there is text to be read, but should not detract the user from the importance of the text. Special care needs to be taken when software is to be used with children with visual handicaps. Many of the best software packages allow teachers to alter colours to provide the best conditions.

Are the rewards suitable for the child and classroom situation?

Incessant tunes and pretty pictures which are often used as rewards for correct responses need to be matched to the children's age and maturity. There is also a need to be able to turn off the sound or even the pictures which can become monotonously boring, and even frustrating after the first few times. However, aural signals can be useful not only to the child, but also to the teacher who can be alerted to a problem on hearing them.

Some of the best software gives these options on a teacher page which can be set before the child uses the program. Levels of sound can be turned off altogether, or adjusted in volume to suit the classroom situation. Where a suitable teacher password is used, there is also no way that the children can alter the settings.

Does the software provide feedback about the child's responses?

Many programs give only a total score at the end of the test. Whilst this gives a superficial analysis of the child's ability, it gives no direct feedback on the questions that caused problems. Of course, the teacher could sit and watch the responses, but this would be impractical in the busy classroom. However it is easily within the computer's power to store all answers and response times, and even analyse them to provide a direct feedback to the teacher.

Documentation

This varies enormously from program to program. Standards have improved enormously and much documentation now comes with extra resources or ideas on making the best use of the software.

Does it do the task better than conventional methods?

This of course is the crucial question. It is important to ask yourself what the computer offering to this activity that cannot be accomplished by more traditional means. In what way does using the computer improve the child's learning?

If there is no advantage in using a particular piece of software, or if the computer is being used merely because it is there, then children may be better off without it. The expensive hardware can certainly be put to better use. However, good quality software which is carefully matched to the needs of the child can be used to great advantage in the classroom.

IT links

The information technology activities outlined in this book can be used to develop and assess children's IT capability as outlined in the National Curriculum. Types of software rather than names of specific programs have been mentioned to enable teachers to use the ideas regardless of the computers used.

Main IT focus
The main emphasis for the development of IT capability within these activities is on communicating and handling information. However, within mathematics there is a wide range of software available to support children's learning and teachers may still want to include specific software which runs on their computer and which addresses the content and understanding of the subject being taught. The activities in this book are very practically based and give children opportunities to use concrete materials and resources to develop mathematical understanding. Content-specific software should not be used to replace such experiences and should be used to develop or reinforce understanding only after initial practical work.

Teachers should also be aware that although such software may assist pupils in their learning of mathematics, it may add little to the development of their pupils' IT capability.

AREA OF IT	TYPE OF SOFTWARE	ACTIVITIES (page nos.)			
		CHAPTER 1	CHAPTER 2	CHAPTER 3	CHAPTER 4
Communicating Information	Word Processor	14,15,20	35,42	64,65	
Communicating Information	Concept keyboard	15	35		
Communicating Information	DTP	15			
Communicating Information	Art/graphics		34,35		
Communicating Information	Framework		34		
Information Handling	Database				78,81,83,84,86,87
Information Handling	Graphing software				86

SOFTWARE TYPE	BBC/MASTER	RISCOS	NIMBUS/186	WINDOWS	MACINTOSH
Word processor	Stylus Folio Prompt/Writer	Phases Pendown Desk Top Folio	All Write Write On	My Word Kid Works 2 Creative Writer	Kid Works 2 EasyWorks Creative Writer
Framework		My world		My World	
Art package	Picture Builder	1st Paint Kid Pix Splash	Picture Builder	Colour Magic Kid Pix 2	Kid Pix 2
Database	Our Facts Grass Pigeonhole Datashow	DataSweet Find IT	Our Facts Datashow	Sparks Claris Works Information Workshop	Claris Works Easy Works
Graphing software	Datashow	Pictogram Picture Point DataSweet	Datagraph	Datagraph Easy Works	Easy Works
Control	Simple four function calculators				

NUMBER

	ENGLISH	SCIENCE	HISTORY	GEOGRAPHY	D&T	ART	MUSIC	PE
NUMBER SYSTEM AND PLACE VALUE	Telling stories. Writing instructions for their peers and teachers.	Noting similarities and differences in materials when sorting and matching, classifying and counting.	Constructing and using a timeline to sequence events.	Learning about number rhymes from different countries. Finding out about number games and puzzles played around the world.	Design and make board games.	Collecting and sorting images and objects, for example, arranging pebbles in order, e.g. from light to dark (attribute recognition).	Simple counting songs and nursery rhymes, for example *Ten Green Bottles*.	
NUMBER RELATION-SHIPS	Predicting outcomes and discuss possibilities in pattern and sequence work. Predicting what happens in stories such as *Rosie's Walk*, *The Very Hungry Caterpillar*.	Sequencing events in order, for example life-cycle of a butterfly.	Sequencing events and objects in order.		Designing and making own number puzzles.	Making repeated patterns using potato cuts, sponges, etc. Creating patterns using square, triangular and rectangular numbers. Looking at patterns in art, for example, wallpaper, wrapping paper.	Use musical instruments to make rhythmic patterns. Clapping patterns.	Making up sequence of movements in PE and dance.
CALCULA-TIONS AND PROBLEM SOLVING	Explaining ideas and possibilities in problem-solving. Writing instructions for number games.	Calculating body measurements – handspans, strides. Comparing body measurements for example, height, weight.		Calculate numbers of hours sunshine/rain in last week.	Designing and making items for class shop.	Dot-to-dot pictures.		
HANDLING DATA	Describing events, observations and experiences. Making simple, clear explanations of choices, giving reasons for actions. Writing lists and observations. Reading computer text.	Use drawing, tables and bar charts to present results of science experiments.		Weather observations and recording. Survey of types of homes we live in.	Using computer databases. Using computer to generate charts, graphs and tables.		Favourite pop songs of children in the class.	Frequency tables, for example *How many times can you bounce a ball?*

160